STUDENT RESOURCE MANUAL

Preliminary Edition

MATHEMATICS
FOR ELEMENTARY TEACHERS
via problem solving

JOANNA O. MASINGILA
Syracuse University

FRANK K. LESTER
Indiana University

PRENTICE HALL Upper Saddle River, NJ 07458

Acquisitions Editor: *Sally Denlow*
Production Editor: *Dawn Blayer*
Supplements Editor: *April Thrower*
Production Coordinator: *Alan Fischer*
Cover Manager: *Paul Gourhan*
Cover Designer: *Liz Nemeth*

© 1998 by **PRENTICE-HALL, INC.**
Simon & Schuster/A Viacom Company
Upper Saddle River, NJ 07458

Printed in the United States of America

10 9 8 7 6 5 4 3 2

ISBN 0-13-889197-4

Prentice-Hall International (UK) Limited, *London*
Prentice-Hall of Australia Pty. Limited, *Sydney*
Prentice-Hall Canada, Inc., *Toronto*
Prentice-Hall Hispanoamericana, S.A., *Mexico*
Prentice-Hall of India Private Limited, *New Delhi*
Prentice-Hall of Japan, Inc., *Tokyo*
Simon & Schuster Asia Pte. Ltd., *Singapore*
Editora Prentice-Hall do Brasil, Ltda., *Rio de Janeiro*

BRIEF CONTENTS

CONTENTS

PREFACE

The *Resource Manual* is intended as a supplement to the *Activity Book*. The purpose of this *Resource Manual* is to provide you with useful information and ideas to better prepare you to teach mathematics in a manner that is consistent with the new view of mathematics instruction promoted in the *Activity Book*. Specifically, each chapter of the *Resource Manual* contains five special features: (1) a chapter overview and outline, (2) historical, cultural, and social notes related to the mathematics you will study in the *Activity Book*, (3) explanations of key mathematical concepts and problems found in the *Activity Book*, (4) a section titled "Where Would I Find This?", and (5) a bibliography of selected books and articles related to the teaching and learning of mathematics. Additionally, at the end of the *Resource Manual* you will find (1) a glossary of important words and terms, and (2) an index.

- ## *Chapter Overview and Outline*

  Each chapter in the *Resource Manual* begins with an overview of the mathematical ideas contained in the chapter and the corresponding chapter in the *Activity Book*. The chapter outline lists the sections that are included in the chapter.

- ## *Historical, Cultural, and Social Notes*

  Unfortunately, many students, especially those in grades 5 and higher, view mathematics as irrelevant, dull, and routine. Good teachers are persons who not only have a firm understanding of the subject matter they are teaching, but also have a good grasp of what it takes to make mathematics interesting and relevant for their students and have a good understanding of the social and cultural role mathematics plays in our everyday lives. Teachers who have this sort of understanding are more likely to do a satisfactory job of preparing their students for the real world outside of school.

  For these reasons, each chapter in the *Resource Manual* includes commentaries whose purpose is to provide you with relevant historical, cultural, and social contexts for some of the key mathematical ideas found in the chapters.

- ## *Explanations of Key Mathematics Concepts, Procedures and Processes*

  As you will quickly notice, the activities in the *Activity Book* do not come with discussions and explanations—to provide this information with the activities would not be in the spirit of helping you become a good problem solver and an independent learner of mathematics. However, we realize that there will be some activities for which you will find it useful to have some notes that explain the important ideas in those activities. You may also find these explanations helpful whenever you wish to review the ideas that you have been studying in a chapter. Consequently, the *Resource Manual* contains these explanations for the mathematical concepts and procedures in each chapter in the *Activity Book*.

- ## *"Where Would I Find This?"*

  An essential goal of any mathematics course for prospective teachers of young children should be to help you develop an understanding of how the mathematical concepts, procedures, and processes considered in the course relate to the mathematics that is taught in the elementary school. With this goal in mind, we have developed a special section titled "Where Would I Find This?" for each chapter. This section includes sample pages from elementary school textbooks that involve the topics considered in the chapter. *[Note: This feature will not appear until the first edition of the book.]*

- ### *Selected Bibliography*

We believe that now is the time for you to begin to collect ideas for classroom use, to deepen your understanding of important mathematical concepts and processes, and to increase your awareness of how to help children learn mathematics. Accordingly, the end of each chapter contains a bibliography of useful books and articles to augment the activities and explanations and the historical/social/cultural notes. These readings have been selected from journals of the National Council of Teachers of Mathematics (especially *Teaching Children Mathematics* and *Mathematics Teaching in the Middle Grades*) and other professional references whose audience is the classroom teacher.

- ### *Glossary*

At the end of this *Resource Manual* there is a list of important words and terms that appear at various places in the *Activity Book* and in the explanation section of the *Resource Manual*. This list will include definitions or descriptions of these words and terms with examples whenever appropriate.

- ### *Index*

The index will assist you in locating words and terms that appear in the *Resource Manual*. An important difference between the index and the glossary is that the index will help you find places in the *Resource Manual* where a word or term is actually used in an explanation.

Joanna O. Masingila

Frank K. Lester

Chapter 0: Learning Mathematics via Problem Solving

Chapter Overview:

Mathematics instruction has changed rather dramatically in recent years. A passive transmission view of the teacher's role has been replaced by one involving students as active participants in the act of "doing" mathematics. This new vision is one where mathematics is seen as a cooperative venture in which students are encouraged to explore, make and debate conjectures, build connections among concepts, solve problems growing out of their explorations, and construct personal meaning from all of these experiences.

This chapter provides overviews of the three *Standards* documents, developed by the National Council of Teachers of Mathematics, in order to help you better understand the nature and extent of the changes being advocated by national leaders. Also in this chapter is a list of "problem-solving" tips that should be useful to you as you strive to improve your own ability to solve mathematics problems. The chapter concludes with a discussion of some reasons why problem solving should be a primary focus of mathematics instruction.

Chapter Outline:

The Reform Movement in School Mathematics: It's Time to Change!

The Changing Nature of School Mathematics
Establishing Standards for Curriculum, Teaching, and Assessment
An Overview of the <u>Curriculum and Evaluation Standards for School Mathematics</u>
An Overview of the <u>Professional Standards for Teaching Mathematics</u>
An Overview of the <u>Assessment Standards for School Mathematics</u>

Problem-Solving Tips

Why Is It Important to Learn How to Solve Mathematics Problems?

THE REFORM MOVEMENT IN SCHOOL MATHEMATICS:
IT'S TIME TO CHANGE!

In 1983, the National Commission on Excellence in Education published *A Nation at Risk: The Imperative for Educational Reform* and awoke a sleeping nation to alarming problems in our schools. Since then scores of reports have analyzed virtually every aspect of this enormous problem. Some have called for changes in the curricula, others for changes in the structure of schools; some have pointed out deficiencies in the ways teachers are educated, while others have examined signs of decay in the social and economic structures of society. All agree that the present ways of doing things must change.

Even before the publication of *A Nation at Risk*, precollege schooling in the United States had been undergoing profound changes in the way children are taught mathematics. The changes had begun because traditional notions of basic mathematical competence had been outstripped by ever-higher expectations of the skills and knowledge of workers. It was generally realized that businesses were no longer seeking workers with strong backs, clever hands, and "shopkeeper" arithmetic skills. To quote from *Mathematics Education: Wellspring of U.S. Industrial Strength*, the report of a symposium of representatives from business, industry, government, and education:

> *Today's worldwide, computer-driven, competitive economy demands workers with thinking skills, workers who can deal with computer terminals, automated equipment, and visual data display; who can make estimates and solve problems; who have a mental "toolkit" of number-managing techniques. The rudimentary skills that satisfied the needs of the workplace in the past no longer suffice. . . . But the standard mathematics curriculum still presents, virtually unchanged, a body of doctrines dating back to the 15th century.*

Today the pace of change in the workplace is being hastened by rapid advances in technology; computerization is replacing nearly every facet of the work environment. At the same time, the calculator and computer are having dramatic effects on school mathematics. In particular, they have drastically reduced the importance of low-level computational skills. Although it remains important for students to master basic computational facts such as 17 - 8 or 6 x 9—these tools assist in mental computations, estimations, and other aspects of numerical reasoning—long, tedious computations have become obsolete.

The demands for higher degrees of mathematical competence coincide with a dramatic decline in student interest and performance in the subject over the past 20 years. The traditional curriculum is obviously not meeting society's needs, or our students' needs. Students—who are really quite bright by the way—are well aware that spending years learning, for example, long division, is not going to be useful to them in later years.

The Changing Nature of School Mathematics

In response to the changes in society, mathematics educators have adopted completely new viewpoints about the nature of mathematics, mathematics instruction, and mathematics learning. Mathematics educators are moving from viewing mathematics as a fixed and unchanging collection of facts and skills to emphasizing the importance of conjecturing, communicating, problem solving, and logical reasoning in mathematics learning. These changes are related to a trend away from viewing learning as human information processing and toward seeing learning as a complex process of personal construction of knowledge. As a result, mathematics teaching is moving away from lecturing, explaining, and rote practice of procedures toward helping students construct their own knowledge through realistic mathematical investigations. Table 1 summarizes the key shifts in thinking that have taken place.

Table 1
Changes in Thinking about the Nature of Mathematics, Mathematics Learning, and Mathematics Teaching

Assumptions about:	Change from the view that:	To the view that:
The nature of mathematics	Mathematics is nothing more than a list of rules, facts, and procedures	Mathematics is a science of patterns
The nature of mathematics learning	Mathematics learning is a cumulative process of gradually adding, deleting, and debugging facts, rules, and skills	Humans construct their knowledge to describe, explain, create, adapt, predict and control what they experience or think about
The nature of mathematics teaching	Teaching involves demonstrating and monitoring student activity and correcting errors	Teaching is an act of enabling students to construct and explore their world (both real and imagined)

Establishing Standards for Curriculum, Teaching, and Assessment

In 1989, after a decade of prolonged conversation among teachers, mathematicians, mathematics educators, business leaders, and others concerned about the state of mathematics instruction in American schools, the National Council of Teachers of Mathematics (NCTM) published the first of three documents that provided standards and a sense of direction for school mathematics curriculum and teaching. The *Curriculum and Evaluation Standards for School Mathematics*, asserts that "to equip students for productive, fulfilling lives in the Information Age, the definition of success in mathematics—the objectives of mathematics—must be transformed." Although the *Curriculum Standards* focuses on curriculum, the report also encourages instruction that places mathematics in contexts that give the ideas and concepts meaning and will turn students into active learners. Indeed, the notion of the student becoming an active "doer" of mathematics, rather than a passive receiver of information transmitted by the teacher is central to the message of this important document.

At about the same time as the publication of the *Curriculum Standards*, another report was released that added further voice to the call for reform. This report, *Everybody Counts: A Report to the Nation on the Future of School Mathematics*, which was published in 1989 by the influential Mathematical Sciences Education Board of the National Research Council, discussed the problems inherent in previous efforts to reform school mathematics, documented the changing character of society, and suggested directions that curriculum and teaching reform should take. Taken together, these two reports galvanized the mathematics education community at all levels (kindergarten through college) to begin working toward a common vision of what school mathematics should be.

In 1991 the *Professional Standards for Teaching Mathematics* was published, followed by the *Assessment Standards for School Mathematics* in 1995. Collectively, these three standards documents provide a complete framework for restructuring mathematics in our nation's schools. Because of the importance of each of these documents, we offer an overview of each.

An Overview of the *Curriculum and Evaluation Standards for School Mathematics*

A standard is a statement that can be used to judge the quality of a mathematics curriculum or methods of evaluation. Thus, standards are statements about what is valued. (NCTM, 1989, p. 2)

To make the mathematics curriculum more appropriate for students, the NCTM has provided a number of standards, divided into four categories, the first three by grade level: K-4, 5-8, 9-12, and Evaluation. Special attention is given to four standards across all grade levels. The first is *problem solving*. Specifically, students should be engaged in the solution of thought-provoking, real-world problems. Not only should students learn to solve but problems, but they should also learn mathematics *via* problem solving, which is the focus of these course materials. The second major standard is *communication*. Knowing mathematics is of little value if one cannot communicate mathematical ideas to other people. NCTM's third major standard is *reasoning*. Among other things, reasoning deals with the ability to think through a problem and to carefully evaluate any solution that has been proposed. The fourth of the major standards involves making *connections*. To really understand mathematics, one must be able to see connections between various mathematical ideas, and between "school" and "real world" mathematics.

The *Curriculum Standards* specifies the key ingredients of a high-quality school mathematics program, but it does not include a list of topics for any grade level, nor does it indicate a "scope and sequence" chart, which is so commonly used by publishers of mathematics textbooks. Tables 2.1 - 2.3 and 3.1 - 3.3 provide a list of the 13 standards for level K-4 and the 13 for level 5-8. (There are also 14 standards for grades 9 - 12.)

Table 2.1
Curriculum Standards for Grades K-4: Nos. 1 - 2

STANDARD	GOAL
1. **Mathematics as problem solving**	In grades K-4, the study of mathematics should emphasize problem solving so that students can: Use problem-solving approaches to investigate & understand mathematical content Formulate problems from everyday and mathematical situations Develop and apply strategies to solve a wide variety of problems
2. **Mathematics as communication**	In grades K-4, the study of mathematics should include numerous opportunities for communication so that students can: Relate physical materials, pictures, and diagrams to mathematical ideas Reflect on and clarify their thinking about mathematical ideas and situations Relate their everyday language to mathematical language and symbols Realize that representing, discussing, reading, writing, and listening to mathematics are a vital part of learning and using mathematics

Table 2.2
Curriculum Standards for K - 4 : Nos. 3 - 9

STANDARD	GOAL
3. Mathematics as reasoning	In grades K-4, the study of mathematics should emphasize reasoning so students can: Draw logical conclusions about mathematics Use models, known facts, properties, and relationships to explain their thinking Justify their answers and solution processes Use patterns and relationships to analyze mathematical situations Believe that mathematics makes sense
4. Mathematical connections	In grades K-4, the study of mathematics should include opportunities to make connections so that students can: Link conceptual and procedural knowledge Relate various representations of concepts or procedures to one another Recognize relationships among different topics in mathematics Use mathematics in other curriculum areas Use mathematics in their daily lives
5. Estimation	In grades K-4, the curriculum should include estimation so students can: Explore estimation strategies Recognize when an estimate is appropriate Determine the reasonableness of results Apply estimation in working with quantities, measurement, computation, & problem solving
6. Number sense & numeration	In grades K-4, the mathematics curriculum should include whole-number concepts and skills so that students can: Construct number meanings through real-world experiences and the use of physical materials Understand our numeration system by relating counting, grouping, and place-value concepts Develop number sense Interpret the multiple uses of numbers encountered in the real world
7. Concepts of whole-number operations	In grades K-4, the mathematics curriculum should include concepts of addition, subtraction, multiplication, and division of whole numbers so that students can: Develop meaning for the operations by modeling and discussing a rich variety of problem situations Relate the mathematical language and symbolism of operations to problem situations and informal language Recognize that a wide variety of problem structures can be represented by a single operation Develop operation sense
8. Whole-number computation	In grades K-4, the mathematics curriculum should develop whole-number computation so that students can: Model, explain, and develop reasonable proficiency with basic facts and algorithms Use a variety of mental computation and estimation techniques Use calculators in appropriate computational situations Select and use computation techniques appropriate to specific problems and determine whether the results are reasonable
9. Geometry & spatial sense	In grades K-4, the mathematics curriculum should include two- and three-dimensional geometry so that students can: Describe, model, draw, and classify shapes Investigate and predict the results of combining, subdividing, and changing shapes Develop spatial sense Relate geometric ideas to number and measurement ideas Recognize & appreciate geometry in their world

Table 2.3
Curriculum Standards for K - 4: Nos. 10 - 13

STANDARD	GOAL
10. **Measurement**	In grades K-4, the mathematics curriculum should include measurement so that students can: Understand the attributes of length, capacity, weight, mass, area, volume, time, temperature, and angle Develop the process of measuring and concepts related to units of measurement Make and use estimates of measurement Make & use measurements in problem and everyday situations
11. **Statistics & probability**	In grades K-4, the mathematics curriculum should include experiences with data analysis and probability so that students can: Collect, organize, and describe data Construct, read, and interpret displays of data Formulate and solve problems that involve collecting and analyzing data Explore concepts of chance
12. **Fractions & decimals**	In grades K-4, the mathematics curriculum should include fractions and decimals so that students can: Develop concepts of fractions, mixed numbers, and decimals Develop number sense for fractions and decimals Use models to relate fractions to decimals and to find equivalent fractions Use models to explore operations on fractions and decimals Apply fractions & decimals to problem situations
13. **Patterns & relationships**	In grades K-4, the mathematics curriculum should include the study of patterns and relationships so that students can: Recognize, describe, extend, and create a wide variety of patterns Represent and describe mathematical relationship Explore the use of variables & open sentences to express relationships

Table 3.1
Curriculum Standards for Grades 5 - 8: Nos. 1 - 5

STANDARD	GOAL
1. Mathematics as problem solving	In grades 5-8, the mathematics curriculum should include numerous and varied experiences with problem solving as a method of inquiry and application so that students can Use problem-solving approaches to investigate and understand mathematical content Formulate problems from situations within and outside mathematics Develop and apply a variety of strategies to solve problems, with emphasis on multistep and non-routine problems Verify and interpret results with respect to the original problem situation Generalize solutions and strategies to new problem situations Acquired confidence in using mathematics meaningfully
2. Mathematics as communication	In grades 5-8, the study of mathematics should include opportunities to communicate so that students can: Model situations using oral, written, concrete, pictorial, graphical, and algebraic methods Reflect on and clarify their own thinking about mathematical ideas and situations Develop common understandings of mathematical ideas, including the role of definitions Use the skills of reading, listening, and viewing to interpret and evaluate mathematical ideas Appreciate the value of mathematical notation and its role in the development of mathematical ideas Discuss mathematical ideas and make conjectures and convincing arguments
3. Mathematics as reasoning	In grades 5-8, reasoning shall permeate the mathematics curriculum so that students can: Recognize and apply deductive and inductive reasoning Understand and apply reasoning processes, with special attention to spatial reasoning and reasoning with proportions and graphs Make and evaluate mathematical conjectures and arguments Validate their own thinking Appreciate the pervasive use and power of reasoning as a part of mathematics
4. Mathematical connections	In grades K-4, the study of mathematics should include opportunities to make connections so that students can: See mathematics as an integrated whole Explore problems and describe results using graphical, numerical, physical, algebraic, and verbal mathematical models or representations Use a mathematical idea to further their understanding of other mathematical ideas Apply mathematical thinking and modeling to solve problems that arise in other disciplines, such as art, music, psychology, science, and business Value the role of mathematics in our culture and society
5. Number and number relationships	In grades 5-8, the mathematics curriculum should include the continued development of number and number relationships so that students can: Understand, represent, and use numbers in a variety of equivalent forms (integer, fraction, decimal, percent, exponential, and scientific notation) in real-world and mathematical problem situations Develop number sense for whole numbers, fractions, decimals, integers, and rational numbers Understand and apply ratios, proportions, and percents in a wide variety of situations Investigate relationships among fractions, decimals, and percents Represent numerical relationships in one- and two-dimensional graphs

Table 3.2
Curriculum Standards for Grades 5 - 8: Nos. 6 -11

STANDARD	GOAL
6. Number systems and number theory	In grades 5-8, the mathematics curriculum should include the study of number systems and number theory so that students can: Understand and appreciate the need for numbers beyond the whole numbers Develop and use order relations for whole numbers, fractions, decimals, integers, and rational numbers Extend their understanding of whole number operations to fractions, decimals, integers, and rational numbers Understand how the basic arithmetic operations are related to one another Develop and apply number theory concepts (e.g., primes, factors, and multiples) in real-world and mathematical problem situations
7. Computation and Estimation	In grades 5-8, the mathematics curriculum should develop the concepts underlying computation and estimation in various contexts so that students can: Compute with whole numbers, fractions, decimals, integers, and rational numbers Develop, analyze, and explain procedures for computation and techniques for estimation Develop, analyze, and explain methods for solving proportions Select and use an appropriate method for computing from among mental arithmetic, paper-and pencil, calculator, and computer methods Use computation, estimation, and proportions to solve problems Use estimation to check the reasonableness of results
8. Patterns and Functions	In grades 5-8, the mathematics curriculum should include explorations of patterns and functions so that students can: Describe, extend, analyze, and create a wide variety of patterns Describe and represent relationships with tables, graphs, and rules Analyze functional relationships to explain how to change in one quantity results in a change in another Use patterns and functions to represent and solve problems
9. Algebra	In grades 5-8, the mathematics curriculum should include explorations of algebraic concepts and processes so that students can: Understand the concepts of variable, expression, and equation Represent situations and number patterns with tables, graphs, verbal rules, and equations and explore the interrelationships of these representations Analyze tables and graphs to identify properties and relationships Develop confidence in solving linear equations using concrete, informal, and formal methods Investigate inequalities and nonlinear equations informally Apply algebraic methods to solve a variety of real-world and mathematical problems
10. Statistics	In grades 5-8, the mathematics curriculum should include exploration of statistics in real-world situations so that students can: Systematically collect, organize, and describe data Construct, read, and interpret tables, charts, and graphs Make inferences and convincing arguments that are based on data analysis Evaluate arguments that are based on data analysis Develop an appreciation for statistical methods as powerful means for decision making.
11. Probability	In grades 5-8, the mathematics curriculum should include explorations of probability in real-world situations so that students can: Model situations by devising and carrying out experiments or simulations to determine probabilities Model situations by constructing a sample space to determine probabilities Appreciate the power of using a probability model by comparing experimental results with mathematical expectations Make predictions that are based on experimental or theoretical probabilities Develop an appreciation for the pervasive use of probability in the real world

Table 3.3
Curriculum Standards for 5 - 8: Nos. 12 - 13

STANDARD	GOAL
12. Geometry	In grades 5-8, the mathematics curriculum should include the study of geometry of one, two, and three dimensions in a variety of situations so that students can: Identify, describe, compare, and classify geometric figures Visualize and represent geometric figures with special attention to developing spatial sense Explore transformations of geometric figures Represent and solve problems using geometric models Understand and apply geometric properties and relationships Develop an appreciation of geometry as a means of describing the physical world
13. Measurement	In grades 5-8, the mathematics curriculum should include extensive concrete experiences using measurement so that students can: Extend their understanding of the process of measurement Estimate, make, and use measurements to describe and compare phenomena Select appropriate units and tools to measure to the degree of accuracy required in a particular situation Understand the structure and use of systems of measurement Extend their understanding of the concepts of perimeter, area, volume, angle measure, capacity, and weight and mass Develop the concepts of rates and other derived and indirect measurements Develop formulas and procedures for determining measures to solve problems

An Overview of the *Professional Standards for Teaching Mathematics*

Unfortunately, a good curriculum is not enough to ensure that students can solve problems, communicate, reason, and make connections in mathematics. For this reason, in 1991 the National Council of Teachers of Mathematics also produced standards for the teaching of mathematics: *Professional Standards for Teaching Mathematics*. A number of themes can be found in the *Teaching Standards*. One major theme is that the role of the teacher is changing from that of a "dispenser of knowledge" to a "facilitator of learning." With respect to problem solving and reasoning, this implies that the teacher should do less lecturing on how to solve specific types of problems and more posing and discussing of a wide variety of non-routine and applied problems. The teacher should also focus on helping students make connections between the mathematics they are learning in school and its application to the workplace or home.

Another important theme of the *Teaching Standards* is its list of major shifts in the environment of the classroom—both the physical and intellectual environment. These shifts are summarized briefly in Table 4.

Table 4
Shifts in the Classroom Environment Promoted by the *Teaching Standards*

Shift from:	Shift toward:
Classrooms as collections of individual students working alone	Classrooms as communities of students working collaboratively
The teacher as the "expert" and only authority to determine what is correct	Use of reasoning and verification to determine what is correct
Rote memorization of facts and procedures	Use of mathematical reasoning and student-generated procedures
Mindless, mechanistic use of algorithms and finding of answers	Use of conjecturing, exploring, testing and problem solving to find answers
Viewing mathematics as an isolated collection of facts and procedures	Viewing mathematics as a connected body of ideas, both within mathematics and in the real world

Tables 5.1 and 5.2 (on the following pages) provide a list and very brief description of the six teaching standards.

Table 5.1
Teaching Standards for School Mathematics: Nos. 1 - 4

STANDARD	GOAL
1. Worthwhile Mathematical Tasks	The teacher of mathematics should pose tasks that are based on: Sound and significant mathematics Knowledge of students' understanding, interests, and experiences Knowledge of the range of ways that diverse students learn mathematics and that Engage students' intellect Develop students' mathematical understandings and skills Stimulate students to make connections and develop and coherent framework for mathematical ideas Call for problem formulation, problem solving, and mathematical reasoning Promote communication about mathematics Represent mathematics as an ongoing human activity Display sensitivity to, and draw on, students' diverse background experiences and dispositions Promote the development of all students' dispositions to do mathematics
2. Teacher's Role in Discourse	The teacher of mathematics should orchestrate discourse by: Posing questions and tasks that elicit, engage, and challenge each student's thinking Listening carefully to students' ideas Asking students to clarify and justify their ideas orally and in writing Deciding what to pursue in depth from among the ideas that students bring up during a discussion Deciding when and how to attach mathematical notation and language to students' ideas Deciding when to provide information, when to clarify an issue, when to model, when to lead, and when to let a student struggle with a difficulty Monitoring students' participation in discussions and deciding when and how to encourage each student and participate
3. Students' Role in Discourse	The teacher of mathematics should promote classroom discourse in which students Listen to, respond to, and question the teacher and one another Use a variety of tools to reason, make connections, solve problems, and communicate Initiate problems and questions Make conjectures and present solutions Explore examples and counterexamples to investigate a conjecture Try to convince themselves and one another of the validity of particular representations, solutions, conjectures, and answers Rely on mathematical evidence and argument to determine validity
4. Tools for Enhancing Discourse	The teacher of mathematics, in order to enhance discourse, should encourage and accept the use of: Computers, calculators, and other technology Concrete materials used as models Pictures, diagrams, tables, and graphs Invented and conventional terms and symbols Metaphors, analogies, and stories Written hypotheses, explanations, and arguments Oral presentations and dramatizations

Table 5.2
Teaching Standards for School Mathematics: Nos. 5 - 6

STANDARD	GOAL
5. Learning Environment	The teacher of mathematics should create a learning environment that fosters the development of each student's mathematical power by: Providing and structuring the time necessary to explore sound mathematics and grapple with significant ideas and problems Using the physical space and materials in ways that facilitate students' learning of mathematics Providing a context that encourages the development of mathematical skill and proficiency Work independently or collaboratively to make sense of mathematics Take intellectual risks by raising questions and formulating conjectures Display a sense of mathematical competence by validating and supporting ideas with mathematical argument
6. Analysis of Teaching and Learning	The teacher of mathematics should engage in ongoing analysis of teaching and learning by: Observing, listening to, and gathering other information about students to assess what they are learning Examining effects of the tasks, discourse, and learning environment on students' mathematical knowledge, skills, and dispositions in order to Ensure that every student is learning sound and significant mathematics and is developing a positive disposition toward mathematics Challenge and extend students' ideas Adapt or change activities while teaching Make plans, both short- and long-range Describe and comment on each student's learning to parents and administrators, as well as to the students themselves

An Overview of the *Assessment Standards for School Mathematics*

[The following discussion of the *Assessment Standards* is a slightly modified version of an article written by Lambdin (in press) for *Mathematics Education: An Encyclopedia*.]

The framework for reforming school mathematics was completed with the publication in 1995 of the third of the NCTM's *Standards* documents. Like the other two *Standards* documents, the *Assessment Standards for School Mathematics* offers a clear statement of philosophy and direction; it is not a collection of "alternative" assessment techniques. The *Assessment Standards,* proposes six "standards" for judging assessments: *mathematics, learning, equity, openness, inferences,* and *coherence.* Each of these standards raises important assessment issues.

Standard 1: Important Mathematics. Almost everyone would agree that useful mathematics assessments must focus on important mathematics. However, the new conceptions of the nature of mathematics, how it is learned, and how it should be taught raise serious questions about the appropriateness of the mathematics reflected in most traditional tests since the mathematics included on those tests is generally far removed from the mathematics actually used in real-world problem solving. Nevertheless, there is still much debate over how to define important mathematics and who should be responsible for doing so.

Standard 2: Enhanced Learning. New views of assessment call for tasks that are a natural part of the curriculum, the notion being that assessment should be an integral part of the learning process rather than an interruption to it. This raises the issue of who should be responsible for the development, implementation, and interpretation of assessments of student performance. Traditionally, both standardized and classroom tests were designed to be as objective as possible. By contrast, the new vision of assessment affords teachers much more responsibility and subjectivity in the assessment process. It assumes that teachers know their students best because teachers have multiple, diverse opportunities for examining student work performed under various conditions and presented in a variety of modes.

Standard 3: Equity and Opportunity. Ideally, assessments should give every student optimal opportunities to demonstrate what he or she knows and can do. In practice, however, traditional standardized tests have sometimes been biased against students of particular backgrounds, socioeconomic classes, ethnic groups, or gender. Equity becomes even more of an issue when assessment results are used to label students or to deny them access to courses, programs, or jobs. More teacher responsibility means more pressure on them to be fair and unbiased in their judgments. Also, efforts to establish national or state performance goals are often met with resistance because of fears that their use in high-stakes assessments cannot help but result in inequities. Thus, it is unclear whether recent trends will actually result in increased or decreased equity in mathematics assessment.

Standard 4: Openness. Testing has traditionally been quite a secretive process in that test questions and answers were carefully guarded and criteria for judging performance were generally set behind the scenes by unidentified authorities. By contrast, many experts today believe that students are best served by assessments where the teacher and students openly discuss expectations and scoring procedures. Traditionally, mathematics courses and tests have often been used as filters—to screen students for entry into programs, courses, and jobs; this helps to explain why test questions were kept secret. However, many argue that assessments today should be designed more to describe student proficiencies and deficiencies, to help in making instructional decisions, or to gauge the overall status of the educational system than to categorize individual students. For such purposes, it is argued, criteria can certainly be made more open.

Standard 5: Inferences. Changes in assessment have resulted in new ways of thinking about reliability and validity as they apply to mathematics assessment. For example, when assessment is embedded within instruction, it becomes unreasonable to expect a standard notion of reliability to apply (that a student's achievement on similar tasks at different points in time should be similar), since it is actually expected that students will learn throughout the assessment. Similarly, new forms of assessment prompt a re-examination of traditional notions of validity. Many argue that it is more appropriate to judge validity by examining the inferences made from an assessment than to view validity as an inherent characteristic of the assessment itself. Nevertheless, it is difficult to know how new types of assessments (e.g., student projects or portfolios) can be used for decision making without either collapsing them into a single score (thereby losing all their conceptual richness) or leaving them in their raw, unsimplified, difficult-to-interpret form.

Standard 6: Coherence. The coherence standard emphasizes the importance of ensuring that assessments are appropriate for the purposes for which they are used. Assessment data can be used for monitoring student progress, making instructional decisions, evaluating student achievement (i.e., assigning grades), or program evaluation. However, the types of data that are appropriate for each purpose may be very different. Policy makers and assessment experts often disagree on this issue: the former may have multiple agendas in mind and expect that all be accomplished by using a single assessment, while the latter warn against using assessments for purposes for which they were never intended.

References

Lambdin, D. V. (in press). Trends and issues in the assessment of student performance. In L. S. Grinstein & S. I. Lipsey (Eds.), *Mathematics education: An encyclopedia.* New York: Garland Publishing.

Mathematical Sciences Education Board/National Research Council. (1989). *Everybody counts: A report to the nation on the future of mathematics education.* Washington, DC: National Academy Press.

National Commission on Excellence in Education. (1983). *A nation at risk: The imperative for educational reform.* Washington, DC: U.S. Government Printing Office.

National Council of Teachers of Mathematics. (1989). *Curriculum and evaluation standards for school mathematics.* Reston, VA: Author.

National Council of Teachers of Mathematics. (1991). *Professional standards for teaching mathematics.* Reston, VA: Author.

National Council of Teachers of Mathematics. (1995). *Assessment standards for school mathematics.* Reston, VA: Author.

Pilarski, J. (1989). *Mathematics education: Wellspring of U.S. industrial strength.* New York: Mariott Hotels.

PROBLEM-SOLVING TIPS

Perhaps the most important goal of this course is to improve your ability to think and reason mathematically. As you gain in confidence to engage in mathematical thinking and reasoning you will also notice that you are becoming better at being able to use the mathematics you know to solve problems. Before you begin to work on the problems in this book, let's consider a few general guidelines, or tips, for solving math problems. Throughout the course as you work on the activities and problems, either with your group or alone, you will want to refer to these tips.

I. Develop Good Understanding of the Problem. In order to be successful in solving any problem, you must understand it well.

Suggestions: (a) Restate the problem in language that is clear and sensible to you; (b) Clarify the question (including any hidden questions); (c) Organize the information (get rid of unneeded information and find needed and assumed information).

II. Devise a Good Plan of Attack on the Problem. Analyze the problem with the goal of identifying a systematic method for solving the problem.

Suggestions: (a) Ask yourself: "Have I ever solved a problem like this one before? In what ways was it like this one? What did I do to solve that problem that might be helpful in solving this one?" (b) Consider the various problem-solving strategies that you have learned —decide if any of them will help; (c) Determine what you want to do first, second, etc.

III. Carefully Carry Out the Plan. Implement the plan of attack that you have chosen, being careful to make sure that you are implementing it correctly.

Suggestions: (a) Check your work along the way as you proceed with your solution effort; (b) Don't be content to check only your computations. Also, check to make sure that you are using all the important information and that you have not misinterpreted anything; (c) Ask yourself: "Is this plan getting me anywhere? Am I following the plan I chose, or am I getting sidetracked? Should I abandon this plan and try to think of another way to solve the problem?"

IV. Evaluate Your Solution and Think About What You Have Learned. Decide if the solution is reasonable and consider what you have learned by solving the problem, not only about mathematics, but also about yourself as a doer of mathematics.

Suggestions: (a) Check your solution with the important information; (b) Check all your computations and other work one more time; (c) Think about the plan you used and ask yourself: "Could I have solved this problem another, better way? Would my plan work if the numbers were larger? Would my plan work in general? Could I now solve other problems similar to this one?"

Why Is It Important to Learn How to Solve Mathematics Problems?

Why should children study mathematical problem solving? A complete answer to this question is not possible in a brief chapter section, but central to an answer is our belief that engaging children in problem-solving activities: (a) provides them with opportunities to extend their thinking processes, and (b) encourages them to make mathematical connections among the problems they are asked to solve. In this section we discuss these two reasons by investigating a particular problem that has been considered in numerous articles during the past ten years.

The problem we have chosen is rich enough to present a challenge to students at almost any level, illustrates the great variety of approaches that can be used to solve many mathematical problems, and also brings to light numerous connections among seemingly unrelated problems.

Problem: Eight children are entered in a table tennis tournament. If each child plays one game with each of the other children in the tournament, how many games will be played altogether?

Depending on their age, students might suggest various ways to solve this problem: acting it out , drawing eight dots to represent children and using connecting lines to show games played (see Figure 1), giving the children names and making a list (see Figure 2), considering how many games there would be if there were only two children, only three children, and so on.

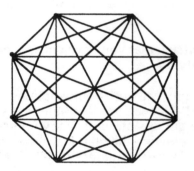

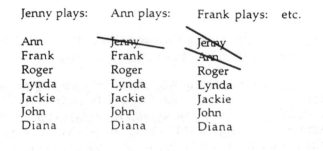

Jenny plays:	Ann plays:	Frank plays:	etc.
Ann	~~Jenny~~	~~Jenny~~	
Frank	Frank	~~Ann~~	
Roger	Roger	Roger	
Lynda	Lynda	Lynda	
Jackie	Jackie	Jackie	
John	John	John	
Diana	Diana	Diana	

Figure 1. A diagram of the
table tennis problem

Figure 2. An organized list of the table
tennis problem

Or, students might simply reason logically: if each of the eight children plays a game with each of the seven others, then there are 8 • 7 games, but since each game involves two players there are only 56 ÷ 2 = 28 different games.

A successful teacher of problem solving encourages flexibility in students' thinking by helping them to agree on labels for the strategies listed above, and then by referring to these strategies again whenever they are used in a new problem situation. Expert teachers of mathematical problem solving go even further than merely encouraging diversity in approaches and helping students to recognize and label strategies. They also encourage students to explain their solutions, to justify their choice of strategy, and to consider in retrospect what different strategies might have been employed. In addition to having children reexamine their thinking, it is often instructive to consider, as well, how the solution would change if alterations or extensions were made to the original problem.

As an example of extending a problem, let's reconsider the problem about the eight children playing table tennis. If the students have solved the problem either by acting it out or by using a diagram, they may simply have counted to get the answer. Extending the problem by asking "what if there were more people, for example, 20 or even 100?" forces a rethinking of the limitations of the initial approach and may prompt a search for a generalization that could be extended to any number of persons. It might be observed that the 20th child would play 19 other children, the 19th child would have just 18 more people to play (since he has already played the 20th child), the 18th child would play just 17 more people, etc. This observations leads to the generalization that the sum n + (n-1) + (n-2) + ... + 1 will give the solution for n+1 persons. But how can we find this sum? The original problem has now been transformed and extended to a new problem.

The great mathematician K. F. Gauss is credited with an ingenious solution to the problem of summing the first 100 whole numbers, a solution that can be understood—and perhaps even discovered—by young children. (Gauss himself was only a child when he discovered it.) Gauss envisioned pairing the numbers as shown in Figure 3. Since each of the 50 pairs sums to 101, the sum is 50(101) or 1/2(100)(101). In general, the sum of the first n integers can be shown to be 1/2(n)(n+1).

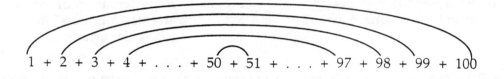

$$1 + 2 + 3 + 4 + \ldots + 50 + 51 + \ldots + 97 + 98 + 99 + 100$$

Figure 3. Gauss's method for summing consecutive whole numbers

Another interesting way to extend many problems is to attempt a geometric solution to a numerical question or vice versa. Children could visualize the sum of the whole numbers 1 to n as a set of stairs. For example, Figure 4 represents 1 + 2 + 3 + 4 + 5. We wish to find the total number of squares that make up the staircase. If we visualize another identical set of stairs and place it upsidedown on top of the first, we get Figure 5. We can easily find the number of squares that make up this figure since the figure is a rectangle with dimensions 5 x 6. But since the rectangle was constructed of two staircases, it contains twice as many squares as we desired to count. The number of squares desired is 1/2(5 • 6). More generally, for a staircase with n steps there would be 1/2(n)(n+1) squares.

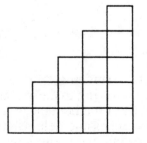

Figure 4. Showing 1+2+3+4+5
as a staircase

Figure 5. Showing 1+2+3+4+5
= 1/2 x (5 x 6)

Teachers need to encourage children to look for connections between newly encountered problems and previously solved problems. Consider the square numbers (1, 4, 9, 16, . . .). They are called square because these are the only numbers of dots that can be arranged in square arrays (see Figure 6). It is easy to see that the nth square number is n^2. A student might ask, "what numbers would be triangular numbers?" They are those numbers of dots (1, 3, 6, 10, . . .) that can be arranged in triangular arrays (see Figure 7). The question might be asked, "How can we find the nth triangular number?" Some children might observe that we find, for example, the 5th triangular number by adding a row of 5 dots to the 4th triangular number. With this observation, it becomes clear that the nth triangular number can be found by summing the numbers $1 + 2 + 3 + . . . n$. Other students might simply recognize the triangular arrays of dots as another way of representing the table tennis-Gauss-staircase problem!

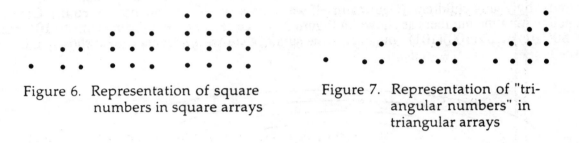

Figure 6. Representation of square numbers in square arrays

Figure 7. Representation of "triangular numbers" in triangular arrays

We have discussed the table tennis problem and some of its many variations to illustrate several points about why students should study problem solving. This very simple problem illustrates how problems can be extended to provide students with opportunities to investigate a variety of ways to think about and to represent them. And the problem variations also show how to engage children in exploring mathematical connections among problems that might otherwise seem to be completely unrelated.

Chapter 1: Getting Started in Learning Mathematics via Problem Solving

Chapter Overview:

Most mathematics educators agree that problem solving is a very important, if not the most important, goal of mathematics instruction at every level. In this chapter you can learn about a historical, social, and cultural context for problem solving, and examine six of the most commonly used problem-solving strategies.

Big Mathematical Ideas:

> problem-solving strategies, generalizing, verifying, using language & symbolism

NCTM Standards Links:

> *K - 4:*   Mathematics as problem solving; Mathematics as reasoning; Mathematical connections; Patterns & relationships

> *5 - 8:*   Mathematics as problem solving; Mathematics as reasoning; Mathematical connections; Patterns & functions

Chapter Outline:

> Historical/Social/Cultural Notes about Problem Solving
> Explanations Concerning Problem Solving
> > *Section 1.1*   Guess and Check
> > *Section 1.2*   Use a Visual Aid
> > *Section 1.3*   Look for a Pattern
> > *Section 1.4*   Work Backwards
> > *Section 1.5*   Use Algebra
> > *Section 1.6*   Solve a Simpler Problem
> > *A Word on Other Strategies*
> Bibliography

Historical/Social/Cultural Notes about Problem Solving

A set of nine playing cards with face values ranging from 1-9 is placed in the following order:

By interchanging two cards at a time, arrange the cards in the correct numerical order. What is the minimum number of such moves that you must make to get the right order?

The above problem is one version of an interesting and well-known problem that highlights an important concept in mathematics. How did you go about trying to solve it initially? Did you need to modify or change your initial strategy? Take a moment to reflect on the process that you followed in order to solve this problem. Can you break this process down into steps? How did you know when you had reached a correct solution to the problem? Do you believe that there may be other ways of solving this problem? Could the problem and the solution be generalized, that is, given any arrangement of nine cards, can you always find a minimum number of moves to arrange it in the correct numerical order? Could you do this for any given number of cards?

The entire procedure that we have discussed above—the process of understanding and solving the problem as well as the questions that followed—is a brief glimpse into the world of a professional mathematician and her (or his) daily work. Often, the mathematics community will describe it in a simple phrase, namely, problem solving.

Problem solving is not a novel idea in mathematics. There are examples of problems being posed and solved in many ancient cultures. What is new about the idea of problem solving is the fact that more and more people are coming to believe that solving problems is at the very heart of learning mathematics. This course is inspired by this belief. Thus, in this course, you will not only learn new concepts but review familiar ones via the process of problem solving.

The famous mathematician, George Polya, wrote a landmark treatise on problem solving in mathematics in 1945. His work, entitled, *How to Solve it*, categorized the entire process of mathematical problem solving into a four step process. These four steps and a brief description of each is given below.

1. *Understand the problem.* This step involves gaining comprehension of the problem, and seeing it clearly as a whole, rewording the problem if necessary, or drawing a picture to understand the information that is contained in the problem as well as what the goal of the problem is intended to be.

2. *Devise a plan.* Once the problem is clearly understood, the problem solver must look about for a strategy to solve it. Such strategies may be based on intuition, or on previous experience and former knowledge. Often, the formulation of a clear strategy to solve a problem is the main achievement of the entire process. One may need to make several unsuccessful attempts before a feasible plan can be found. Strategies for solving problems may include such diverse tools as drawing a picture, devising a simpler problem, simulating a physical situation, building a model, or simply guessing and checking.

3. *Implement the plan.* At this stage, a general plan for solving a problem must be worked out to fit the details of the problem. The plan must be implemented step by step while ensuring that all the conditions in the problem are satisfied.

4. *Look back and review*. This important step involves reflecting on the solution and the path from the problem to the solution. It has two important purposes. It ensures that the solution is correct and fulfills all the conditions of the problem. Secondly, by going over the entire process, one consolidate one's knowledge and ensures that an efficient solution has been reached.

While the four steps seem almost chronological in order, it is important to remember that one may need to go back and forth between the different steps before a solution is achieved. It would be useful to remember these steps as you go through the problems in this course. A conscious reflection on the strategies that you use to solve problems will not only help you become a better problem solver, but also give you a deeper insight into the problems, and help you to connect different areas of mathematics as you learn.

Mathematical problem solving is not an easy task; in fact, it may often prove arduous. But, like at any other skill, if one is persistent, one begins to get better at it. An analogy by Martin Gardner may help to stress the point.

At first sight a new piece of music may look like a confusing array of black dots.
But as the musician works on it, one section at a time, it gradually takes on a shape
of its own, revealing internal connections which had previously been overlooked.
The same is true of an unfamiliar mathematical problem. At first sight you may not
even understand the question. But as you painfully try to make sense of the
problem, you will find that, little by little, the fog begins to lift.

Explanations Concerning Problem Solving

In mathematics, there are several standard strategies that can help in the process of problem solving, when applied appropriately. We will discuss some of these strategies here. As you read through this section, study the examples with care, and work through the problems for each strategy. Also, try and see if there are alternate strategies that you may be able to come up to solve the problems.

Section 1.1—Guess and Check

As the name suggests, this strategy consists of guessing the answer to a problem, and then verifying whether the solution you guessed satisfies all the conditions of the problem. This strategy works particularly well if there are only a limited number of possible answers to choose from. For example, if you are given nine specific numbers to place in a 3 by 3 square without repetition such that the sum of the numbers in any row or column or along any diagonal is always the same, it would help you to start by guessing at some of the number positions and then working with that guess. At other times this strategy may not give you the solution directly. However, it will help you to eliminate some possibilities, and suggest where you may look for possible solutions. Work the two examples that follow and see if you find the guess and check strategy helpful.

<u>Example 1</u>: Place four pennies on the 4 x 4 grid given below in such a way that no two pennies are in the same row, column or diagonal. (Note: The diagonals include the diagonals of all 2 x 2 or 3 x 3 grids that can be extracted from the grid.)

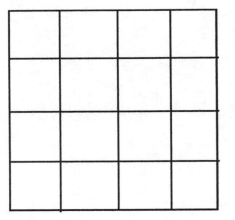

<u>Solution</u>: The following are the only possible solutions, as you can see by using the guess and check strategy.

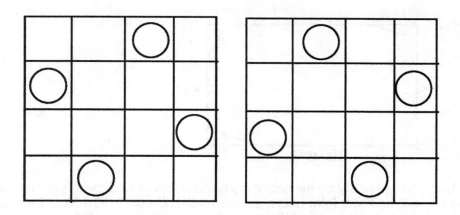

Example 2: Sophia has 5 more dimes than she has quarters. If the total amount of money that she has is $4.70, how many coins of each type does she have?

Solution: She has 12 quarters and 17 dimes.

Section 1.2—Use a Visual Aid

There are different ways in which one can use a visual aid in order to look for a solution to a problem. Such visual aids include drawing a picture, using physical manipulatives, or even connecting the problem to some situation that you have experienced in your life so that you can make sense of it using your own experience.

Drawing a picture or a diagram is particularly useful when the problem one is dealing with involves a physical situation. A picture will help to show the relative position of various objects in the problem. Often, it is also a useful way to organize the given information. Once you have drawn a picture, it can help you to interpret the problem and the conditions in it. It may also suggest a possible strategy to solve the problem. While it may not be always essential, it is usually helpful for you to draw a clear and well-labeled picture. Firstly, such a picture is easier to interpret, and secondly, seeing all the information in one place may make it easier to find a solution.

Similarly, one may use such physical manipulatives as tiles, pencils, candy, boxes, cones, or cans in order to understand a problem or to look for a solution. These manipulatives may be particularly useful in case your problem involves three dimensional objects or moving objects from one place to another when looking for a solution. Work through the following examples to help you understand the use of these strategy.

Example 3: John is supposed to run 4 laps around a rectangular field that measures 100 by 85 feet. However he feels a little lazy and cuts across the corners each time, leaving each side 12 feet before the edge, and hitting the other side 5 feet from its edge. By what distance has John cut short his run?

Solution: It is easy to see that, in this case, drawing the field and marking the distances on it would help to see the problem more clearly and to find its solution.

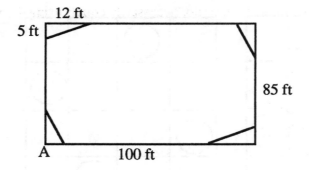

Once this picture is clear, one can easily do the necessary calculations to find the answer to the question. For one lap around the field, John runs a distance = 2(100+ 85) = 370 feet. Each time he cuts across a corner, instead of running for (12 + 5) feet, he actually runs a distance of only 13 feet (Why?), so for one lap he actually runs a distance of (starting at point A on the picture and going counterclockwise)

((100 − (12 + 5)) + 13 + (85 − (12 + 5)) + 13) x 2 (Why?)
= 354 feet.

Thus, in one lap, John cut his run short by 370 feet − 354 feet = 16 feet. So, in 4 laps he cut his run short by 4 x 16 = 64 feet.

    While in the above case, it was quite obvious that the above picture was the one to draw, sometimes (a) it helps to draw a picture even if one is not explicitly called for, and (b) different people may draw different pictures for the same problem. Consider the following problem.

Example 4: The Tennis Club is organizing a tournament. It has 7 members. In the tournament, each of the members must play each of the other members three times. How many games are played in the tournament altogether?

Solution: Let us say the members are A , B, C, D, E, F, and G.
Consider the following pictures that two students drew to solve the problem.

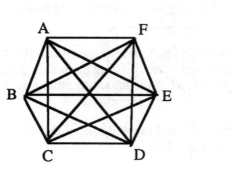

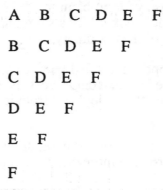

Use either of these pictures or draw one of your own to solve the problem asked above.
Answer: 45 matches.

Now, try and solve the following problem using a picture.

<u>Example 5</u>: Divide a round cake into 11 parts (not necessarily equal) using 4 straight cuts.

<u>Solution</u>:

<u>Example 6</u>: Take the ace, 2, 3, 4, 5, 6, 7, 8, 9 and 10 of any one suit from a pack of cards and put them in a stack in your hands. Now, you will do the following. You will take the topmost card and place it face up on the table, then take the next card and place it at the bottom of the stack. You will continue to do this until all the cards are face up on the table. How will you arrange the stack in your hands so that the first card you place on the table is the ace, the next card is a two, the next a three and so on.

<u>Solution</u>: The order of the cards will be ace, 6, 2, 10, 3, 7, 4, 9, 5, and 8.

Section 1.3—Look for a Pattern

Another useful strategy that often helps in looking for a solution to a problem is looking for patterns. This strategy is particularly useful when one is trying to generalize an idea or to look for an algebraic formula. The strategy is to look at specific cases of the solution of a problem, and to see if an identifiable pattern emerges. Once one has identified the pattern, it is usually a good idea to verify it with other randomly chosen instances before one feels reasonably convinced of it. Here's an example that will help to illustrate this strategy.

<u>Example 7</u>: Given n points in a plane, no three of which are collinear, how many line segments must be drawn to connect all pairs of points?

<u>Solution</u>: As you read the problem, what is your initial plan to solve it? Perhaps the best thing to do is to actually take points in a plane and connect them by line segments. It is always useful to make such trials systematically. So, we start with two points (one point of course is irrelevant in this case), then take three points, then four, and so on. Try drawing the relevant pictures, and see if your trials match the values in the following table.

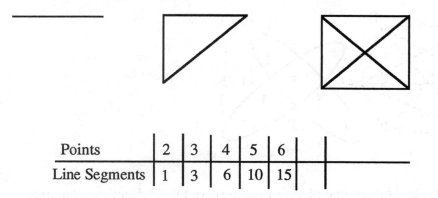

Points	2	3	4	5	6		
Line Segments	1	3	6	10	15		

Does the table help you to find a general solution? Let us take a look.

For 2 points, we had one line. At the next stage, with three points, we added two more to get a total of three lines. At the next stage with four points, we added three more lines to get a total of six lines and so forth. Let us write this down in another table.

Points	2	3	4	5	
Line Segments	1	1+2	1+2+3	1+2+3+4	

From this table the pattern becomes clear. For 3 points, we have 1+2 line segments; for 4 points we have 1+2+3 line segments, and so on. Thus, for n points, we will have $1+2+3+ \ldots + (n-1)$ line segments. This gives us the general formula to find the number of segments that connect any number of (non-collinear if more than two) points, in pairs, to each other.

For this problem, we notice that we actually used two strategies. We started by drawing pictures, and used the information from the specific cases to build a table that would display the information in a compact form. The second table is an attempt to identify the relevant pattern. Of course, this part of the problem may take some time and effort since a pattern may not be obvious at first. You may have to play around with the information you obtain from specific cases, and may also need to do a larger number of cases before you can find the connections between the specific cases. In this sense, finding the pattern may be like solving a picture puzzle. You may need to find several pieces before you can see what the entire picture is going to be. Here are other problems where finding the pattern will help you solve the problem.

Example 8: For the array shown below, continue the pattern to get two more rows for it.

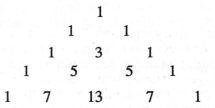

Solution: There may be different answers depending on the patterns observed by different people. One such pattern shows that the first and last digits in each row is 1, and that successive odd numbers lie along the diagonals. Such numbers as 13 are obtained by juxtaposing the two numbers above it (in the third row—the 1 and the 3)

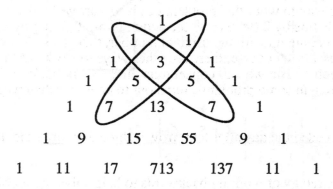

Example 9: A slice of potato, assumed to be circular for convenience, is to be cut up into small pieces by straight knife cuts. The pieces are not to be rearranged or piled up between cuts. What

is the greatest number of pieces that can be produced by a given number of cuts? (Note: We shall take a very thin slice so that cuts are made only on the flat surface of the slice.)

Solution: The cuts must be drawn in such a way that each successive cut intersects every cut before it. Also, only two lines can meet at any given point of intersection. (See a similar problem discussed under Section 1.2—Use a Visual Aid.) If n represents the number of cuts, then the number of pieces obtained are given by n(n +1)/2 + 1.

Example 10: How many diagonals are there in a regular n-sided polygon?

Solution: The number of diagonals in a regular n-sided polygon is given by
n(n − 1)/2 − n = n(n − 3)/2

Each of these problems will require possibly more than one strategy for you to be able to solve the problem. Try and connect the problems that you are doing now with other similar problems that you may have done before, either in other mathematics classes or in activities done in this class. The importance of making such connections cannot be overemphasized. They will not only give you ideas on how to solve the problems given here but will also help you to build a bigger picture.

Section 1.4—Work Backwards

Suppose you visit a friend in an unfamiliar city. Your friend gives you directions to reach her house from the highway. After spending some time with her, you are ready to return. This time you need to reach the highway from your friend's house but you do not have a map. All you have are the directions your friend gave you to reach her house. What would you do to get back to the highway?

The obvious solution to your problem is to try and work backwards from the directions given to you earlier. You could either recreate the route you took in your head just like a movie and play it backwards (if you are good at remembering roads) or you could write down the directions in the reverse order. Thus, you will begin with your friend's house as your starting point, and reverse the order of the roads you traveled on. You will also need to reverse the actions you took at each point, so that if you turned left at a particular crossroads, you will now need to turn right at the same point. If you are careful and do not make any mistakes, you are sure to reach the highway by this process.

The strategy that you used in the problem given above works very well with certain mathematical problems. For example, suppose April is thinking of a number. If you add 7 to the number, multiply the result by 2 and then subtract 10, you get 26. What was the original number that April thought of? One way to work this problem out is to start with 26, and add 10. This gives us 36. Now we divide this by 2 (to reverse the action of multiplying by 2), and this gives us 18. We now subtract 7 and come up with the original number, that is 18 - 7 = 11. So, the number that April was thinking of is 11. Of course, there are other ways to work out this problem; for example, one could use algebra. But we will concentrate on the work backwards strategy for this section. Working backwards, in some problems, turns out to be easier than working through algebra.

Example 11: What day preceded the day after tomorrow if three days after the day before yesterday will be Sunday?

Solution: We will use the strategy of working backwards to help solve the problem. We are told that Sunday is three days from the day before yesterday. Therefore, we count back three days from Sunday to get Thursday as the day before yesterday. This makes today a Saturday. Thus, the day after tomorrow will be Monday, and so the day that preceded the day after tomorrow will be one day before Monday, that is, it will be Sunday.

The strategy of working backwards assumes that you have already arrived at the solution of the problem. You must then work backwards towards the original problem in a series of steps to be able to see the solution. Now, try solving the following problems using similar strategies.

<u>Example 12</u>: On an ordinary die, the numbers 1 and 6, 2 and 5, and 3 and 4 are on opposite sides. In how many ways can a die be marked subject to this condition? We will assume that the orientation of the die is immaterial. Thus, if you can rotate the die in any direction without changing the relative position of the numerals on the different sides, the arrangement is regarded as a single one. Hint: Assume that you already have all such dice with the different faces marked. Now, either draw the various dice or try and visualize them in your head to see how the different sides will be marked.

<u>Solution</u>: There are two ways in which a die may be marked subject to the given condition.

<u>Example 13</u>: Tim and Angela went to play with their friend Robert at his house. Robert's mother gave them a bowl of M & M's. Angela took one-third of the candy, but feeling a little guilty about taking so many, she put back 2. Tim then took one-third of the remaining, but returned 2 for similar reasons. Robert then took half of the remainder, but he did not like brown M&M's so he put back the two he had picked up. When the children were done, there were 9 candy pieces left (which they ate up later, of course). How many pieces of candy had there been in the bowl originally?

<u>Solution</u>: There were 24 pices of candy to begin with.

Section 1.5—Use Algebra

Using algebra is probably one strategy that every student in high school becomes familiar with in order to solve problems. in fact, often, algebra is the only strategy that students try to use to solve a problem. While not all problems can be solved using algebra, it certainly is a very useful problem-solving tool, particularly when it is combined with other strategies, such as drawing a picture, making a table, or looking for patterns. Just as a reminder, this strategy involves replacing an unknown quantity (or quantities) with a variable (or variables) using letters such as x or y, setting up equations using these variables to satisfy the condition given in the problem, and then solving the equation for the variable using symbolic manipulation. In fact, as one brilliant scientist, while he was still a young child, was told by his father, "algebra is a lazy man's arithmetic—you pretend that you know a quantity that you really don't, and you play around with it until you find that you have found the quantity that you only pretended to know earlier." The little boy was so impressed with his father's words that he picked up an algebra book and solved all the problems in the book using this technique!

In spite of this inspiring example, we shall only try to solve some problems here with the help of algebra. Take a look at the examples, and then try to solve the other problems given. You may need to brush up the rules for operations with algebraic symbols before you begin.

<u>Example 14</u>: Show that the sum of any five consecutive multiples of 3 is a multiple of 15.

<u>Solution</u>: We can write a multiple of 3 as 3m, where m is any integer. Then the next multiple of 3 will be 3m + 3, and so on. Thus, five consecutive multiples of 3 can be written as 3m, 3m + 3, 3m + 6, 3m + 9, and 3m + 12. Their sum will be 3m + (3m + 3)+ (3m + 6)+ (3m + 9) + (3m + 12) = 15m + 30 = 15(m + 2), which is clearly a multiple of 15.

Example 15: Sam was arranging vases of flowers at the tables in his restaurant in preparation for the evening meal. The tables were arranged for either 4 guests at a table or 5 guests at a table. Sam had 22 vases, and he put 1 vase at each table for 4 and 2 vases at each table for 5. If the restaurant could seat a total of 70 people, how many tables of each kind were there?

Solution: Let x represent the number of tables for 4, and y represent the number of tables for 5. Then, we get, $x + 2y = 22$ (Why?) and $4x + 5y = 70$ (again, why?). Thus, we need to solve the system of equations

$$x + 2y = 22$$
$$4x + 5y = 70.$$

The first equation when multiplied by 4 gives $4x + 8y = 88$.
Subtracting the second equation from this one, we get $3y = 18$, so that $y = 6$.
Substituting $y = 6$ in the first equation, we get, $x + 2 \cdot 6 = 22$, so that $x = 22 - 12 = 10$.
Thus, there were 10 tables for 4, and 6 tables for 5.

Example 16: Find the area of the following figure:

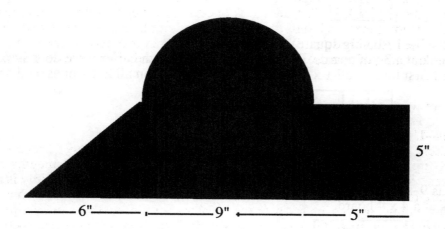

Solution: Area of figure is approximately 116.8 square inches. One way to look at this figure is to divide it into a right triangle (with legs of length 6" and 5" and an area of 15 square inches), a rectangle (with dimensions of 14" and 5" and an area of 70 square inches), and a semi-circle (with a radius of 4.5" and an area of approximately 31.8 square inches).

Example 17: Elissa and Jennifer are painting a room in the house. Elissa can paint the entire room by herself in 3 days, and Jennifer can do the same in 4 days. How long will it take them to paint the room together?

Solution: They can paint it in 12/7 or 1 5/7 of a day.

Section 1.6—Solve a Simpler Problem

Sometimes, when one looks at a mathematical problem, it may seem overwhelming simply because it has too many conditions that need to be satisfied, or big, complex numbers or simply too many tasks that need to be done to get the final answer. In such case, it may be easier to look for an easier, related problem to solve. Once you find the solution to the easier problem, you can examine its solution, and see what insight it gives you for the big, complex problem. Often, this process may make your task much easier.

The problem, however, is that it may not always be immediately apparent what an easier, related problem may be. Certainly, if the numbers look big and strange, or have a large decimal part to them, you may look at easier numbers to work with. If there are too many conditions, you may try to relax one (or more) of them. If there are too many tasks in the problem, you may want to identify several smaller tasks, or subgoals, and look to satisfy them.

Once again, remember, you will need other strategies that you have learned. A problem usually becomes much easier to solve if you have all the necessary tools at your command. So, try and see if there are other strategies that you may be able to combine to solve your problem.

<u>Example 18</u>: How many squares are there on a 8 x 8 checkerboard?

<u>Solution</u>: To find the total number of squares (certainly more than 64) on an 8 x 8 checkerboard may be difficult to do directly. Instead, we shall try to solve a simpler problem by looking at smaller boards. We start with a 2 x 2 board.

This board has 4 + 1 (the big square) = 5 squares.
Now, let us look at a 3 x 3 board. The counting will be much easier if we do it systematically. Thus, we shall first look at all 1 x 1 squares in the board, then all 2 x 2 ones, and so on.

This board has 9 + 4 + 1 = 14 squares (check and see)
We now look at a 4 x 4 board.

Here, we have 16 + 9 + 4 + 1 = 30 squares.
Do you now see the pattern?
Let us put the information we have in a chart.

Size of board	Number of squares	Total
1 x 1	1	1
2 x 2	1 + 4	5
3 x 3	1 + 4 + 9	14
4 x 4	1 + 4 + 9 + 16	30

We can rewrite $1 + 4$ as $1^2 + 2^2$; $1 + 4 + 9$ as $1^2 + 2^2 + 3^2$, and $1 + 4 + 9 + 16$ as $1^2 + 2^2 + 3^2 + 4^2$. This makes the pattern clear. For a 5 x 5 board, we should have $1^2 + 2^2 + 3^2 + 4^2 + 5^2 = 55$ squares, and so on. Thus, for a 8 x 8 checkerboard, we should have $1^2 + 2^2 + 3^2 + 4^2 + 5^2 + 6^2 + 7^2 + 8^2 = 204$ squares.

Notice that in the above problem, we used a variety of strategies. We tried a simpler, related problem, drew pictures, organized the data into a chart, and looked for a pattern. Each of these steps brought us a little closer to the solution. Now, try the following problems.

Example 19: It has been exactly one thousand days since Harry last met Sally. If today is a Friday, on what day did they last meet?

Solution: They last met on a Saturday.

Example 20: Judy's home and school are situated on the opposite corners of a diagonal of a rectangular grid of city blocks (see picture below). She bikes to school every day. Bored with riding the same path daily, she decides to vary her route each day. However, she would not like to ride any more than she has to. After how many days will she have to repeat a route?

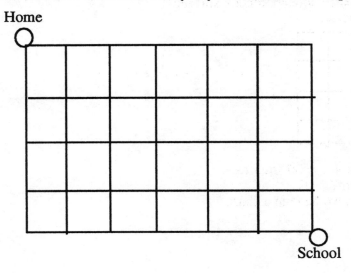

Solution: 210 days

A Word on Other Strategies

The list of strategies compiled above is by no means exhaustive, but it does provide you with a handy set of tools that you will need as you do the problems in this book or even mathematical problems that you may encounter outside the classroom. There are many other strategies that you may develop yourself as an aid. Such strategies may include keeping organized lists (as we did in some problems), using graphs or scale drawings, organizing information in matrix forms, and so on. If you do find other strategies that work for you, make sure you make a note of them. You might even want to share such strategies with other people. Discussions with other people are likely to strengthen your own grasp of the strategy, and will also help you to understand why a particular strategy works.

Bibliography

Averback, W. B. & Orin, C. (1980). *Problem solving through recreational mathematics.* New York: Freeman.

Gardiner, A. (1996). *Discovering mathematics: The art of investigation.* New York: Oxford Scientific Publications.

Akaishi, A. & Saul, M. (1991). Exploring, learning, sharing: Vignettes from the classroom. *Arithmetic Teacher, 39,* 12-16.

Bledsoe, G. J. (1989). Hook your students on problem solving. *Arithmetic Teacher, 37,* 16-20.

Borassi, R. (1992). *Learning mathematics through inquiry.* Portsmouth. NH: Heinemann.

Brown, S. I. & Walter, M. I. (1990). *The art of problem posing* (2nd edition). Hillsdale, NJ: Erlbaum.

Brown, S. I. & Walter, M. I. (Eds.). (1993). *Problem posing: Reflections and applications.* Hillsdale, NJ: Erlbaum.

Bush, W. S.& Fiala, A. (1986). Problem stories: A new twist on problem posing. *Arithmetic Teacher, 34,* 6-9.

Campbell, P. F. & Bamberger, H. J. (1990). Implementing the *Standards*: The vision of problem solving in the *Standards. Arithmetic Teacher, 37,* 14-17.

Cemen, P. B. (1989). Developing a problem-solving lesson. *Arithmetic Teacher, 37,* 14- 19.

Charles, R., & Lester, F. K. (1982). *Teaching problem solving: What, why and how.* Palo Alto, CA: Dale Seymour Pub.

Corwin, R. B. (1993). Doing mathematics together: Creating a mathematical culture. *Arithmetic Teacher, 40,* 336-341.

Day, R. P. (1986). A problem-solving component for junior high school mathematics. *Arithmetic Teacher , 34,* 14-17.

Esty, W. W., & Teppo, A. R. (1996). Algebraic thinking, language, and word problems. In P. C. Elliott (Ed.), *Communication in mathematics: K-12 and beyond* (pp. 45-55) Reston, VA: National Council of Teachers of Mathematics.

Fortunato, I,, Hecht, D., Tittle, C. K., & Alvarez, L. (1991). Metacognition and problem solving. *Arithmetic Teacher, 39,* 38-40.

Fulkerson, P. (1992). Getting the most from a problem. *Arithmetic Teacher, 40 ,* 178-179.

Garofalo, J. (1987). Metacognition and school mathematics. *Arithmetic Teacher, 34*(9), 22-23.

Garofalo, J., & Lester, F. K. (1985). Metacognition, cognitive monitoring, and mathematical performance. *Journal for Research* in Mathematics Education, 16, 163-176.

Garofalo, J. & Bryant, J. (1992). Assessing reasonableness: Some observations and suggestions. *Arithmetic Teacher, 40,* 210-212.

Goodnow, J., Hoogeboom, S, Moretti, G., Stephens, M., & Scanlin, A. (1987). The problem solver: Activities for learning problem solving strategies. Palo Alto, CA Creative Publications.

Hembree, R., & Marsh, H. (1993). Problem solving in early childhood: Building foundations. In R. J. Jensen (Ed.), *Research ideas for the classroom: Early childhood mathematics* (pp. 151-170). Old Tappan, NJ: Macmillan.

Hyde, A. A., & Hyde, P. R. (1991). *Mathwise: Teaching mathematical thinking and problem solving*. Portsmouth, NH: Heinemann.

Kersh, M. E., & McDonald, J. (1991). How do I solve Thee? Let me count the ways!" *Arithmetic Teacher, 39,* 38-41.

Kimball, R. L. (1991). Activities: Make your own problems-and then solve them. *Mathematics Teacher, 84,* 647-655.

Kroll, D. L., & Miller, T. (1993). Insights from research on mathematical problem solving in the middle grades. In D. T. Owens (Ed.), *Research ideas for the classroom: Middle grades mathematics* (pp. 58-77). Old Tappan, NJ: Macmillan.

Kruliks S. & Rudnick, J. A. (1985). Developing problem-solving skills. *Mathematics Teacher, 78,* 685-692, 697-698.

Lester, F. K. (1989). Research into practice: Mathematical problem solving in and out of school. *Arithmetic Teacher, 39,* 33-35.

Masingila, J. O. (1997). Let's be realistic. *Mathematics Teaching in the Middle School, 2* (3), 136-137.

Masingila, J. O., & Moellwald, F. E. (1993). Using Polya to foster a classroom environment for real-world problem solving. *School Science and Mathematics, 93*)5), 245-249.

Mason, J., Burton, L. & Stacey, K. (1985). *Thinking mathematically* (Revised edition). Menlo Park, CA: Addison-Wesley.

Matz, K. A. & Leier, C. (1992). Word Problems and the Language Connection. *Arithmetic Teacher, 39,* 14-17.

McNeal, B. (1995). Learning not to think in a textbook-baled mathematics class. *Journal of Mathematical Behavior, 14,* 205-234.

Meyer, C., & Sallee, T. (1983). *Make it simpler: A practical guide to problem solving in mathematics.* Menlo Park, CA: Addison-Wesley.

O'Daffer, P. G. (1984/1985). Problem solving: Tips for teachers. *Arithmetic Teacher 32.*

Sigurdson, S. E., Olson, A T., & Mason, R. (1994). Problem solving and mathematics reaming *Journal of Mathematical Behavior, 13,* 361-388.

Silver, E. A., Kilpatrick, J, & Schlesinger, B (1990) *Thinking through mathematics: Fostering inquiry and communication in mathematics classrooms* . New York: College Entrance Examination Board.

Silverman, F. L., Winograd, K., & Strohauer, D. (1992). Student-generated story problems. *Arithmetic Teacher, 39,* 6- 12.

Stimpson, V. C. (1989). Using diagrams to solve problems. *Mathematics Teacher, 82,* 194-200.

Szetela, W. (1986) The checkerboard problem extended, extended, extended. School Science and Mathematics, *86,* 205-222.

Talton, C F. (1988). Let's solve the problem before we find the answer. *Arithmetic Teacher, 36*(1), 40~5.

Whitin, D. J. (1987). "Problem solving in action: The bulletin-board dilemma. *Arithmetic Teacher, 35, 48-50.*

Chapter 2: Numeration

Chapter Overview:

Among the most important topics in elementary school mathematics are those concerned with systems of recording and naming numbers: numeration systems. . In this chapter you can learn about a historical, social, and cultural context for numeration, and examine some concepts and procedures involving numeration ideas.

Big Mathematical Ideas:

generalizing, problem-solving strategies, decomposing, mathematical structure, representing

NCTM Standards Links:

K - 4: Mathematics as problem solving; Mathematics as communication; Mathematics as reasoning; Mathematical connections; Number sense & numeration

5 - 8: Mathematics as problem solving; Mathematics as communication; Mathematics as reasoning; Mathematical connections; Number & number relationship; Number systems & number theory

Chapter Outline:

Historical/Social/Cultural Notes about Numeration

The earliest roots of mathematics can probably be traced back to a need for counting and recording numbers. From as far back as historians can tell, every society has had some means of recording numerical quantities. This is true even of those societies for which no written records of numerals are available. Evidence of this fact comes from archaeological excavations from different parts of the world.

The handle of a bone tool etched with some clear markings found amongst the remains of the Ishango community in central Africa bear testimony to the fact that this neolithic community had some means of keeping tally of numerical quantities.

Another culture from which archaeologists have dug up evidence of recording numerical quantities is that of the Incas, a culture that flourished until about the fifteenth century A.D., in parts of modern Peru, Bolivia, Chile, Ecuador, and Argentina. The Incas had a device called *quipu* that they used for recording numbers. A quipu consists of a collection of cords, containing knots of different kinds. There are records of a quipu being used as a tool to record data during a household census in 1567.

The earliest system of spoken and written symbols used to represent numbers may have used small numbers such as 2, 3, or 4 as a **base**. The use of such systems has been reported from communities that lived in Africa, southern Australia, and South America.

<u>Definition</u>: A numeration system has a **base** if it reflects a process of repeated grouping by some number greater than 1. This number is called the base of the system, and all numbers in that system are written in terms of powers of the base. If b is the base, numbers are written in terms of 1, b, b^2, b^3, etc.

Numeration systems in early societies often reveal interesting aspects of the culture that prevailed, and what was regarded as important in these societies. The Aztecs of central America had such written symbols for numbers as a blob representing a maize pod for a unit, a diagrammatic sketch of a maize plant to represent the number 400, and (what is commonly believed to be) a maize doll to represent the number 8000. The use of the base 10 in many cultures evolved from the practice of using fingers of the hands for counting. Zulu words for the numbers 1 through 10 are clearly based on this practice. In warmer climates, on the other hand, people could even use their toes for counting and this led to the use of the number 20 as a base, in such cultures as the Maya of central America, and the Yoruba in western Africa.

The Development of the Hindu-Arabic Numeration System

The system of numbers that we use today, called the Hindu-Arabic numeration system, has a fascinating and checkered history. While it is commonly believed to have been invented by Hindu mathematicians in India around 500 A.D., from where it was carried to other parts of the world by the Arabs, it took a long time before it became universally accepted. Meanwhile, in other parts of the world, different civilizations developed different ways of bringing order to their system of numeration. A brief glimpse of these systems, and how each in its own way contributed to the advancement of human understanding of numbers is given below.

The Egyptian Numeration System

The Egyptian system of numbers dates back to about 3400 B.C. Our information on this civilization is derived from papyrus documents that the Egyptians used for record keeping. They used ink brushes to write upon the papyrus. Initially, it was a simple system based on using a series of vertical strokes, called tally marks, the number of which was in one to one correspondence with the items being counted. Later, this cumbersome method was improved upon by using some system of grouping numbers bigger than 9. The Egyptians drew upon their environment to introduce pictographic symbols to represent the different powers of 10, from 10^1 to 10^7. The following table shows these Egyptian numerals.

Egyptian Numeral	Description	Hindu-Arabic Equivalent
	vertical staff	1
	heel bone	10
	scroll	100
	lotus flower	1,000
	pointing finger	10,000
	polliwog or burbot	100,000
	astonished person	1,000,000

<u>Definition</u>: A symbol used to represent a number is called a **numeral**. For example, the symbol "3" is a numeral that represents the quantity three.

Numbers written in the Egyptian system used an additive property. Thus, the value of the number was the sum of the values of the numerals used to write the number. The following example illustrates this idea.

	represents	100,000
	represents	20,000
	represents	400
	represents	30
	represents	1

Thus, represents 120,431

The Babylonian Numeration System

The Babylonian numeration system developed at about the same time as the Egyptian but it has been much better preserved because of the use of clay tablets, as opposed to papyrus, by the Babylonians. They used a reed, shaped at one end, to make wedge shaped marks on wet clay. Once these tablets dried, the marks on them were preserved for posterity.

The most outstanding achievement of the Babylonian numeration system was the invention of a place value system, that is, a numeration system in which the value of a numeral depended on its placement with respect to other numerals while writing a number. The Babylonians used the following symbols.

Babylonian Numeral	Hindu-Arabic Equivalent
▼	1
‹	10

These symbols were combined to write numbers as, for example, ‹‹‹▼▼ represented 32. Numbers greater than 59 were represented using repeated groupings of 60. Spaces were used to separate multiples of powers of 60. The following examples illustrate this idea.

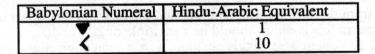 represents $30 \cdot 60 + 1$, or 1801

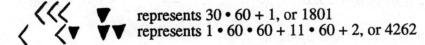 represents $1 \cdot 60 \cdot 60 + 11 \cdot 60 + 2$, or 4262

The Babylonian system was somewhat confusing as it lacked the concept of zero, until about 300 B.C. Thus, ▼▼▼ could represent $3 \cdot 60$ or 3.

The Chinese Numeration System

The Chinese civilization, in about 1300 B.C., had a system of numeration that was simpler and in many ways more advanced than most contemporary civilizations. This is because, in this system, it was possible to write any number, however large, by the use of ten basic symbols, along with three additional ones to represent 20's, 100's and 1000's. The following table shows the symbols used by this civilization.

Chinese Numeral	Hindu-Arabic Equivalent
	1
	2
	3
	4
	5
	6
	7
	8
	9
	10
	100
	1,000

Here is an example of 247 written using the Chinese system

(a)
(100)
(4)
(10)
(7)

$$2(100) + 4(10) + 7 = 247$$

The Mayan Numeration System

The Mayan system, developed about 400 B.C., was one of the most economical ones developed. It used only three symbols, given in the table below.

Mayan Numeral	Hindu-Arabic Equivalent
•	1
—	5
⊜	0

The Mayan system was a base 20 system. Numbers were written vertically in this system, with the greatest values on top. One of the curious feature in this system was the value of the symbols in the third position from the bottom. Keeping in mind the fact that this was a base 20 system, the value of the symbol in this position should be a multiple of 20^2, or 400. However, it appears that the Mayans used $20 \cdot 16$, or 360, in this position. It has been conjectured that the number 360 may have been used because it is the approximate length of the calendar year (18 months consisting of 20 days each, with an additional 5 unlucky days). Given below are some examples of numbers written in the Mayan system.

$$7 \cdot 360 = 2520$$
$$12 \cdot 20 = 240$$
$$6 \cdot 1 = \underline{6}$$
$$2766$$

$$6 \cdot 360 = 2160$$
$$0 \cdot 20 = 0$$
$$3 \cdot 1 = \underline{3}$$
$$2163$$

The Roman Numeration System

The Roman system of numeration is one of the few ancient ones that continues to be in use today. It can be seen on the faces of some watches and clocks, on cornerstones, and in the names of monarchs.

The table given below shows the numerals used in the Roman numeration system.

Roman Numeral	Hindu-Arabic Equivalent
I	1
V	5
X	10
L	50
C	100
D	500
M	1000

An additive property is used to combine numerals. Thus, MDLXII represents $1000 + 500 + 50 + 10 + 2 = 1562$. Similarly, DCCXX1 represents 721.

A subtractive property was introduced in this system in order to avoid writing a symbol more than three times. This was done by placing symbols representing smaller numbers to the left of symbols representing larger ones, as, in writing 4 as IV, instead of IIII, or 900 as CM, instead of VIIII.

A limited multiplicative property is also evident in the Roman numeration system. A bar placed over a symbol indicates that the value of the symbol must be multiplied by 1000. Thus

$\overline{\text{V}}$ represents 5000, and $\overline{\text{CDX}}$ represents $410 \cdot 1000$.

More than one bar can be placed over symbols to indicate multiplication by greater powers of 1000. Thus,

$\overline{\overline{\text{CX}}}$ represents $60 \cdot 1000 \cdot 1000$.

The Hindu-Arabic Numeration System

The Hindu Arabic numeration system used today originated in India. While different versions of this system existed even earlier, a system which is very close to the system we know today, developed around 850 A.D.

The Hindu-Arabic system is a base ten system, and hence is said to be a decimal system (*decem* is a Latin word indicating ten). It has ten basic symbols called digits: 0, 1, 2, 3, 4, 5, 6, 7, 8, and 9. In this system, all numbers can be written as a combination of these digits. It is a place value system, where the place values are based on groupings by powers of 10.

Each digit in a numeral has two main functions. The digit indicates its face value, and its position in the numeral indicates its place value. Thus in the number 247, the symbol "4" has a place value of four, and being in the second place from the right in the number, it represents $4 \cdot 10$. Similarly, "2" represents the face value of two, and by its place indicates that it represents $2 \cdot 10^2$. The system becomes clear when numbers are written in their expanded form. For example,

$$65031 = 6 \cdot 10^4 + 5 \cdot 10^3 + 0 \cdot 10^2 + 3 \cdot 10^1 + 1$$

Explanations Concerning Numeration

Section 2.1—Numbers, Numerals and Names

A *number* is an idea that represents a quantity. A *numeral* is the symbol we use to represent a number. For example, the symbol "5" represents the quantity of five. A *name* of a number is the word that we use to call the number or numeral. Different languages use different names to represent the same quantity or idea.

Section 2.2—Face Value and Place Value

The numerical quantity represented by the symbol for a digit is called its *face value*. For example, the symbol 3 in all the numerals—234, 88834, and 23—represents the numerical quantity three.

When we talk about a place value system, we mean a numeration system in which the position of a digit determines its value. The Hindu-Arabic system is a place value system. Thus, the same digit placed in different positions in a numeral represents different multiples of the digit and hence has different values. We then say that that digit has different place values in the different numerals. The *place value* of a digit is a description of its positioning in that numeral.

In the Hindu-Arabic system, we usually represent numbers in base ten. Thus, when writing numbers, the digit to the far right represents units (or just the numerical value of the digit itself). The second digit from the right represents ten times the value of that digit. Similarly, the third digit from the right represents 100 times the value of that digit, and so on. Let us clarify this idea with an example.

Example 1: Look at the numerals 3, 35 and 3147. In what place value is 3 in each of these numerals?

Solution: In the first numeral 3 is the only digit in the numeral. In the second numeral, 3 is in the second position from the right, and in the third number, 3 is in the fourth position from the right. By placing 3 in these different positions, we are making it represent different values. Thus, in the first case, the digit 3 represents just the number 3. In the second number, the digit 3 represents 10 times 3 or the number 30, while in the third number the digit 3 represents 1000 times 3 or the number 3000. Thus, if we were looking at the place value of 3 in the three different numerals, then in the first case, we will say that the place value of 3 is "units," in 35, we will say it is "tens," and in the numeral 3147, the place value of 3 is "thousands." We could also say that 3 is in the units, tens and thousands place respectively in these three numerals.

Section 2.3—Place Value in a Base Other Than Ten

In a base ten system, we group by tens. Therefore, the place value of a digit in a base ten system is given by multiplying the digit by a power of ten; that is, if the digit is in the far right position we multiply the digit by the 0th power of 10 (a rather complicated way of saying multiply by 1, but we are trying to be consistent with the terminology); if the digit is in the second position from the right, we multiply it by the first power of ten (that is by 10 itself); if the digit is in the third position from the right, we multiply it by the second power of ten (that is by 100), and so on.

Suppose the base we are using is different from ten. So, let us say we are using a base n, where n could be any positive integer. In that case, the place value of a digit in a numeral will be given by multiplying the digit by a power of n. Thus, to get the place value of a digit in the base n system, if a digit is in the far right position, we will multiply the digit by the 0th power of n (that is, by 1); if a digit is in the second position from the right, we multiply it by the first power of n (that is by n itself); if the digit is in the third position from the right, we multiply it by the second power of n (that is by n^2), and so on. Let us now look at an example.

Example 2: Consider the numeral 1232_{four} (by putting "four" in the subscript we are indicating that the numeral is written in base 4). What are the place values for the different digits in this numeral?

Solution: In this numeral, the 2 in the far right position represents 2 times 4^0, which is just 2; the 3 represents 3 times 4^1, or 12; the 2 in the third position from the right represents 2 times 4^2, which is 2 times 16, or 32, and the 1 represents 1 times 4^3, which is 1 times 64, or 64. Thus, instead of having increasing powers of 10 (in base ten), we have increasing powers of 4 as we move left from the far right digit in a numeral.

While there is no standard terminology to indicate the place value in a different base, we could, for example in the above case, say that the 2 in the far right place is in the units place (or it has the place value units), the 3 is in the fours place (or that it has the place value fours), the second 2 is in the sixteens place (or that it has the place value sixteens), and so on. This terminology would be consistent with the terminology we use for base ten.

Section 2.4—Expanded Notation
This form of notation refers to writing a number in a form that shows the value of each digit in that numeral.

Example 3: Write the number 7354 in expanded notation

Solution: $7354 = 7 \cdot 10^3 + 3 \cdot 10^2 + 5 \cdot 10^1 + 4 \cdot 10^0$

Using the same kind of notation, we could write a numeral in any base in expanded notation.

Example 4: Write 7026_{nine} in expanded notation.

Solution: $7026_{nine} = 7 \cdot 9^3 + 0 \cdot 9^2 + 2 \cdot 9^1 + 6 \cdot 9^0$

Section 2.5—Conversions From One Base to Another
While we usually write numbers in base ten; sometimes it is necessary to write numbers in other bases. It is not difficult to convert numerals from one base to another. However, here, we shall restrict ourselves to converting a numeral from a given base to base ten, and vice versa.

We will illustrate the process of converting a numeral from a given base to base 10 using an example.

Example 5: Convert the numeral 4357_{eight} to base ten.

Solution: We start by writing the given numeral in expanded notation. It is then easy to calculate the value of the number in base ten.

Thus, we have
$$4357_{eight} = 4 \cdot 8^3 + 3 \cdot 8^2 + 5 \cdot 8^1 + 7 \cdot 8^0$$
$$= 4 \cdot 512 + 3 \cdot 64 + 5 \cdot 8 + 7$$
$$= 2048 + 192 + 40 + 7$$
$$= 2287$$

Thus, $4357_{eight} = 2671$ in base ten

Now we will consider how to convert a numeral from base ten to a given base. Once again, we shall give an example to illustrate the process.

Example 6: Suppose we want to convert the numeral 427 (in base ten) to a number in base five.

<u>Solution</u>: Step 1: We first seek the highest power of 5 that is less than or equal to the given number. Thus, we are looking for the highest power of 5 that is not greater than 427. Some of the powers of 5 in increasing order are 1, 5, 25, 125, 625, ... The greatest of these numbers that is less than 427 is 125, which is 5^3.

Step 2: We now look for the greatest multiple of 125 that is less than or equal to 427. This turns out to be 3 (3 • 125 = 375 ≤ 427 but 4 • 125 = 500 > 427). This will be the far left digit in the number that represents 427 in base five.

Step 3: Subtract 3 • 125 from 427. Thus, we get, 427 − 375 = 52.

Step 4: Consider the next lower power of 5 than we had in step 1. This turns out to be 2 ($5^2 =$ 25). Find the closest multiple of 25 that is less than or equal to 52. This, we find is 2 (since 2 • 25 is 50). Thus, the second digit from the left (that is, the digit to the left of 3 obtained in step 2) will be 2. Subtract 50 from 52. This gives us 2.

Step 5: Repeat step 4 with decreasing powers of 5 and the result you get in the preceding step until you get to the 0th power of 5. In this case, working with 2 (the result of step 4) and the next lower power of 5, that is 5^1, we find that 5 is greater than 2. Thus, we get the third digit from the left in the representation of 427. This will be 0.

Step 6: Now, we look at the next lower power of 5 which is 5^0, which is just 1 (of course, this number should be less than 5). Thus, the far right digit in the number 427, written in base five will be 2.

Hence, the number 427 written in base five will be 3202_{five}.

Here is another way to do the same process.

427 = 5 • 85 + 2 (Divide 427 by 5. This gives a quotient of 85, and a remainder 2)
85 = 5 • 17 + 0 (Divide 85 by 5. This gives a quotient of 17, and a remainder 0)
17 = 5 • 3 + 2 (Divide 17 by 5. This gives a quotient of 3, and a remainder 2)

Thus, 427 = 3202_{five}

    Let us describe this process in words. To convert a number from base ten to a given base, say n, divide the number by n. This will give you a quotient and a remainder. The remainder is the far right digit in the required number written in base n. Now, divide the numerator from the previous step by n again. This will again give you a quotient and a remainder. The remainder is the second digit from the right in the required number. Divide the numerator by n again. Repeat this process until the quotient you get is smaller than the base. Then the final quotient will be the far left digit in the required number, and the remainders, written in the reverse order in which you got them give you the rest of the number. Here is another example to illustrate the above process.

<u>Example </u>7: Convert 2560 from base ten to base eight.

<u>Solution</u>: The following steps will give us the required number.

2560 = 8 • 320 + 1
320 = 8 • 40 + 0
40 = 8 • 5 + 0
Thus, 2560 = 5001_{eight}

Section 2.6—Computations in Different Bases

Just like with numbers in base ten, we can perform the basic arithmetic operations with numbers in other bases. We shall restrict ourselves to addition, subtraction, and multiplication (as you might guess, division is a more complicated process, and so we shall ignore it!). We shall illustrate the different operations with examples.

Addition in a base other than 10: The basic difference between addition in base ten and addition in a different base, say n, is that when you add two digits having the same place value, you must carry over to the next place every group of n (instead of every group of ten as in base ten) that you get by this operation.

Example 8: Perform the operation $2446_{eight} + 5675_{eight}$

Solution: As in addition with base ten, we start with the far right digits, and carry over to the next place (on the left) every group of eight that we get when we add two digits. Thus, in this case, we start by adding 6 and 5, which is 13, that is one group of 8 and 3 units. So, we keep the 3 units and carry over 1 (the group of 8) to the next place. Here, we get 1 (the part carried over) + 4 + 7, which is 14, that is, one group of 8 and 4 units. We retain the 4 units and carry 1 to the next place. Here, we get 1 + 4 + 6, which is again 13, so that again we retain 3, and carry over 1. So, now, in the far left spot, we get 1 + 2 + 5, which is 10, that is one group of eight and 0 units. So, here, we retain 0 and carry over 1. Therefore, we get $2446_{eight} + 5675_{eight} = 10343_{eight}$

Subtraction in a base other than 10: Just as in subtraction, addition is very similar to addition in base ten. The basic difference between subtraction in base ten and subtraction in a different base, say n, is that when you borrow 1 from the next higher place, you must remember that you are borrowing a group of n and not ten (as in base ten).

Example 9: Perform the operation $E536_{twelve} - 58T_{twelve}$

Solution: We start with the far right digits, where we have to subtract T (the digit that will represent the number eleven in base twelve) from 6. Since this is not possible, we need to borrow one group of 12 from the next higher place in the number. Thus we borrow 1 from 3, so that here we are left with 2. In the far right column, we now have to subtract T from 10 + 6 = 16, which is 8. Thus, 8 will be the far right digit in the result of the operation. In the second place from the right we now have to subtract 8 from 2 (left from 3 after we borrowed 1). Once again, we need to borrow 1 from the next higher place. This leaves us with 4 in the third place from the right in the first number, and we can now subtract 8 from 10 + 2 = 12, which gives us 6. Now, in the third place from the right we have to subtract 5 from 4 (left from 5 after subtracting 1). Once again we need to borrow 1 from E, leaving behind T, and obtaining E when we subtract 5 from 10 + 4 = 14.

Thus, we get $E536_{twelve} - 58T_{twelve} = TE68_{twelve}$. You may need to write this entire process in the familiar column form to understand the procedure.

Multiplication in a base other than ten: Once you have learned addition and subtraction in base ten, multiplication becomes easier. Once again, the important point to remember is that each time, the grouping must be done by the number that is the base.

Example 10: Perform the operation $234_{six} \cdot 75_{six}$.

Solution: We start with the far right digits. We get $4 \cdot 5 = 20$, which is equal to 3 groups of six, and 2 units or 32. We retain 2, and carry the 3 over to the next higher place. Here, we get $3 \cdot 5 = 15$, which is equal to 2 groups of six and 3 units or 23. We add 3 (that was carried over) to 23, and get 30, which is 3 groups of six and 0 units. Thus we get 0 for this place, and we carry 3 to the next place. Here, we get, $2 \cdot 5 = 10$, which is equal to 1 group of six and 4 units or 14, we

add 3 to 14, and get 21, which is 2 groups of six and 1 unit. Thus, we get $234_{six} \cdot 5_{six} = 2102_{six}$.
Writing this in the column form in which we usually perform multiplication in base ten, and
completing the multiplication, we will get the following.

$$
\begin{array}{r}
234_{six} \\
\times\ 45_{six} \\
\hline
2102_{six} \\
+\ 14240_{six} \\
\hline
20342_{six}
\end{array}
$$
(Remember the addition here is in base six)

Bibliography

Arithmetic Teacher. (1988, February). Focus issue on early childhood mathematics, *35*.

Beattie, Ian D. "Building Understanding with Blocks. *Arithmetic Teacher* 34 (October 1986): 5- 11.

Burton, G. M. (1984). Teaching the most basic basic. *Arithmetic Teacher, 32*, 20-25.

Ewbank, William A. "LCM—Let's Put It in Its Place." *Arithmetic Teacher* 35 (November 1987): 45-47.

Flexer, R J. (1986). The power of five: The step before the power of ten. *Arithmetic Teacher, 34*(3), 5-9.

Frank, A. R. (1989). Counting skills—A foundation for early mathematics. *Arithmetic Teacher, 37*, 14-17.

Gluck, D. H. (1991). Helping students understand place value. *Arithmetic Teacher, 38*, 10-13.

Harrison, M. & Harrison, B. (1986). Developing numeration concepts and skills. *Arithmetic Teacher, 33*, 18-21.

Ifrah, G. (1987). *From one to zero: A universal history of number*. New York: Penguin Books.

Krusen, K. (1991). A historical reconstruction of our number system. *Arithmetic Teacher, 38*, 46-48.

Labinowicz, E. (1985). *Learning from children: New beginnings for teaching numerical thinking*. Menlo Park, CA: Addison-Wesley.

Menninger, K. (1992). *Number words & number Ssmbols: A cultural history of numbers*. New York: Dover.

Payne, J. N., & Huinker, D. M. (1993). Early number and numeration. In R. J. Jensen (Ed.), *Research ideas for the classroom: Early childhood mathematics* (pp. 4~71). Old Tappan, NJ: Macmillan.

Rathmell, E. E. & Leutzinger, L. P. (1991). Implementing the *Standards*: Number representations and relationships. *Arithmetic Teacher, 38*, 20-23.

Sutton, J. T. & Urbatsch, T. D. (1991). Transition boards: A good idea made better. *Arithmetic Teacher, 38*, 4-9.

Suydam, M. N. (1986). Research report: The process of counting. *Arithmetic Teacher, 33*, 29.

Thompson, C. S. (1990). Place value and larger numbers. In J. N. Payne (Ed.), *Mathematics for the young child* (pp 89-108). Reston, VA: National Council of Teachers of Mathematics.

Thompson, C. S., & Van de Walle, J. A. (1984). The power of 10 *Arithmetic Teacher, 32*(3), 6-11.

Thompson, C. S. (1989). Number sense and numeration in grades K-8. *Arithmetic Teacher, 37*, 22-24.

Wearne, D., & Hiebert. J. (1994). Place value and addition and subtraction. *Arithmetic Teacher, 41*, 272-274.

Zepp, R. A. (1992). Numbers and codes in ancient Peru: The Quipi. *Arithmetic Teacher, 39*, 42-44.

Chapter 3: Operations with Natural Numbers, Whole Numbers & Integers

Chapter Overview:

A solid understanding of addition, subtraction, multiplication, and division is crucial to being able to do mathematics and these operations play central parts in the elementary school mathematics curriculum. In this chapter you can learn about a historical, social, and cultural context for operations, and examine some concepts and procedures involving operation ideas.

Big Mathematical Ideas:

mathematical structure, verifying, generalizing, using algorithms

NCTM Standards Links:

K - 4: Mathematics as problem solving; Mathematics as communication; Mathematics as reasoning; Mathematical connections; Concepts of whole number operations; Whole number computation

5 - 8: Mathematics as problem solving; Mathematics as communication; Mathematics as reasoning; Mathematical connections; Computation & estimation

Chapter Outline:

Historical/Social/Cultural Notes about Operations

The period from 500 A.D. to 1400 A.D. is often referred to as the "Dark Ages" in the history of western civilization. There was little progress in learning, or the arts. All the mathematical progress at this time was contributed by the Hindus and the Arabs. Two major achievements of this time are credited to the Hindus. The first of these was the invention of zero as a full-fledged digit (earlier the zero had been used only as a place holder). The second idea that revolutionized arithmetic was the invention of the negative numbers. Interestingly, the idea of negative numbers arose not from any practical applications, but from the desire to apply a rule without any exceptions. The Hindus studied algebraic equations to which one could find positive solutions, such as, $x + 3 = 5$, and then they found equations that were similar but for which they could find no positive solutions, such as $x + 3 = 2$. Thus, in about 900 A.D., they found it necessary to invent negative numbers, a contribution that proved to be of immense importance for later mathematicians.

The Hindu numerals and the Hindu-Arab methods of computation were carried to the west by travelers and traders. It is one such traveler, Leonardo of Pisa* (1175 - 1250), who is credited with writing a book inspired by these methods, the *Liber Abaci*, that finally converted Europe to Hindu-Arabic arithmetic. The book is also said to have inspired a deluge of manuals on elementary computations and commercial arithmetic since the fifteenth century.

While this flood of manuals had no influence whatsoever on the progress of mathematics, a search for quicker, and more efficient methods of computation than manual ones resulted in the invention of such tools as the abacus, slide rules, and the counting board. Finally, a 19th century English mathematician and inventor, Charles Babbage, invented a machine, called the Difference Engine, to calculate and print multiplication tables. While the Difference Engine itself was a failure, it is considered by many to be the forerunner of the modern computer, and Babbage is now universally acknowledged as being the father of modern computers.

The credit for being the first person to detail the process now known as computer programming, however, goes to a woman, Ada Byron Lovelace. While Lovelace began her career by translating into English Babbage's work on another machine regarded as the precursor to the modern computer, the Analytic Engine, she soon established her own mathematical prowess. Even within the cloistered confines of 19th century English society that did not regard mathematics as a suitable pursuit for young women, Ada Lovelace proved herself an intellectual equal to many of her peers.

Modern computing has of course come a long way since the times of Babbage and Lovelace. It can now perform such wonderful feats as calculating the value of π to thousands of digits, factoring huge numbers that were at first considered prime, and solving problems whose solutions could only be guessed at before, such as the Four-Color Problem! Why bother? One important reason is that while at first the solution of such problems only seems to bring pleasure to the inveterate number cruncher, eventually many of them find use in such practical applications as the developing security codes, and checking the speed and efficiency of new computing tools.

---

* Leonardo is more famously known as Fibonacci. While he is credited with other mathematical work as well, he is most famous for the series of numbers named after him, called the Fibonacci Sequence (which is discussed in Activity 4.15).

Explanations Concerning Operations

Group Properties

In this chapter, you will come across different properties of the various sets of numbers, such as the properties of closure, identity, and associativity. These kinds of properties are called group properties as they refer to a mathematical structure called a group. We give below the definitions of some of these properties. These properties are always defined in relation to an operation such as addition or subtraction. Thus, while giving examples we shall choose one of these operations.

Section 3.1—Closure Property for a Set

We say a given set is closed under a given operation if, when you take any two elements of the set and perform the operation on it, the result of the operation is still an element of the set. This must always be true no matter which two elements of the set you take.

Example 1: Is the set of natural numbers closed under addition?

Solution: The set of natural numbers (that is, the set $\{1, 2, 3, \dots \}$) is closed under addition, because, the sum of any two numbers in this set is always an element of this set. However, this set is not closed under subtraction, because, if you, for example, subtract 2 from 1, the result is -1, which is not an element of this set.

Section 3.2—Commutative Property for a Set

We say that a given set is commutative under an operation if the order in which you perform the operation on any two numbers in the set is irrelevant; that is, you get the same answer no matter in which order you perform the operation. Algebraically, we may state this condition as follows: A set is said to be commutative under the operation * if $a * b = b * a$ for any two elements a and b in the set.

Example 2: Is the set of natural numbers commutative under addition?

Solution: The set of natural numbers is commutative under addition because, regardless of the order in which you add two numbers, their sum will be the same.

Section 3.3—Associative Property for a Set

We say a set is associative under a given operation, if, given any three elements of the set, the results of the following procedures is the same.

Procedure 1: Take the first two elements, and perform the operation on them. Then take the result of the first operation and the third element and now perform the operation on them.

Procedure 2: Take the last two elements, and perform the operation on them. Now, take the first element, and perform the operation on this element and the result of the operation in the previous step.

Algebraically, we may state this condition as follows:

$(a * b) * c = a * (b * c)$, where a, b, and c are any three elements of the given set, and * is the operation under discussion. Thus, if this condition is satisfied, then we say that the set is associative under the operation *.

Example 3: Is the set of natural numbers associative under multiplication?

Solution: The set of natural numbers is associative under multiplication, since if you take any two elements in the set and multiply them, and then multiply the product you obtain with a third element, the answer you will get will be the same as when you multiply the first element with the product obtained when you multiply the second and third element. But this set is not closed under subtraction. Why?

Section 3.4—Identity for a Set

We say a given set has an identity under a given operation if the set has a unique element, say I, so that when you perform the operation with this element and any other element, say x, in the set, the result of the operation is x. Algebraically, we say that the set has an identity I, under the operation *, if, for any element x in the set, we find, I * x = x * I = x. It is important to note that the element I should be unique. If such an element exists, we say that I is the * identity for that set.

Example 4: Does the set of whole numbers have an additive identity?

Solution: We say that 0 is the additive identity for the set of whole numbers, because, if you add 0 to any whole number, you get the whole number again.

Section 3.5—Inverse of an Element in a Set

Consider a set that has an identity under a given operation. We say that an element, say x, belonging to this set has an inverse, if, for that element, we can find another element, say y, in the same set so that, when we perform the operation on x and y, the result is the identity of the set for that operation. Algebraically, we say, that an element x has an inverse under the operation * in a given set with * identity I, if we can find an element y in the same set so that x * y = y * x = I. If such an element exists, we say that y is the * inverse of x, and vice versa.

Example 5: Does every element in the set of integers have an additive inverse?

Solution: Every integer has an additive inverse because, for any integer x, you can find the element -x, so that x + (-x) = (-x) + x = 0 (the additive identity for integers). However, a whole number does not have an additive inverse within the set (of whole numbers).

Section 3.6—Distributive Property for a Set

Consider a set with two operations, say * and Σ. We say that the operation * distributes over the operation Σ, if , for any three elements, say a, b , and c in the set, we have the following:

$$a * (b \Sigma c) = a * b \Sigma a * c$$

Example 6: Does the distributive property hold for addition and multiplication on the set of natural numbers?

Solution: Multiplication distributes over addition for the set of natural numbers because, if we take any three natural numbers, say a, b and c, we find

$$a \bullet (b + c) = a \bullet b + a \bullet c$$

(You may check this out for several different numbers) However, addition does not distribute over multiplication in the same set (Once again, you may check this by looking at some examples).

Models of Operations

Mathematicians often use physical models in order to illustrate a concept or understand a problem. Such models may also serve to show the same concept from different perspectives. In this section, we will build some simple but useful models in order to illustrate the concept of operations on whole numbers, and the different approaches to the same operation that one may take, depending on a specific problem.

Section 3.7—Addition

We will use two types of models to illustrate the process of addition. As you will see, we will also use these two models to model subtraction, multiplication and division.

The model below is called the *set model* and represents the addition of 4 and 3. Consider two disjoint sets, A and B, where set A has 4 objects, and set B has 3 objects. We form their union, set C. Set C has 7 objects which represents the total objects in sets A and B.

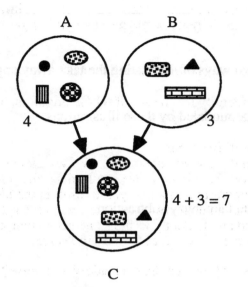

We can also represent addition as a *measurement model*, using a whole-number line.

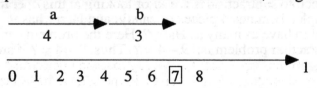

On the number line, l, whole numbers are represented by the points labeled 0, 1, 2, etc. The distance from 0 represents the magnitude of the number. The arrow pointing right indicates that the whole numbers are unending, and increase infinitely.

In the above model, the arrow a represents 4 (its length is 4 units), while b represents 3. These arrows are placed end to end, starting at 0 to represent addition, and the sum is represented by the total, which is 7.

Section 3.8—Subtraction

There are different ways of looking at subtraction, depending upon the problem. We will look at each of these approaches, one by one.

Take Away Approach

Set Model   Measurement Model

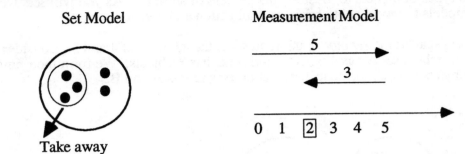

Take away

The two models above represent two ways of illustrating the take away approach to subtraction.

1.   Write a word problem that could be modeled by these illustrations.

2.   Explain why this approach is called take away subtraction.

Missing Addend Approach
    The missing addend approach to subtraction is a way of looking at this operation as the reverse process of addition. For example, Tom has 4 pieces of candy, and Harry has 9. How many more pieces of candy does Tom need to have as many as Harry? Here the problem can be written as: $4 + ? = 9$. The equivalent subtraction problem is: $9 - 4 = ?$ Thus, $9 - 4 = ?$ if and only if $4 + ? = 9$.

    Here are two ways of modeling this approach.

Set Model   Measurement Model

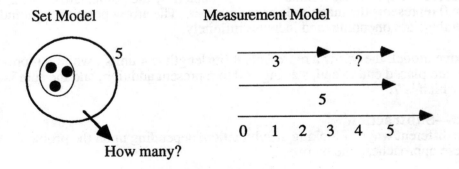

How many?

3.   Write a word problem that could be modeled by these illustrations.

4. Can we always be assured of a whole number answer if we use the missing addend definition of subtraction? Explain your answer.

Comparison Approach

There is a third approach to the process of subtraction. This approach arises out of such problems as: Jennifer has 7 pencils, and Mark has 3. How many more does Jennifer have than Mark? Thus, this approach is called the comparison approach.

5. Sketch the set and measurement models for this kind of subtraction.

6. Write a word problem that could be modeled by your sketches.

Section 3.9—Multiplication

As with subtraction, there are several different approaches to multiplication.

Repeated Addition Approach

This way of defining multiplication can be illustrated by the following problem: Fran and Judy start a book club in their school. They buy 5 books at the beginning of each month. How many books will the club have at the end of 4 months? This problem can be expressed as $5 + 5 + 5 + 5 = 20$, or $4 \cdot 5 = 20$.

Here are the set and measurement models to illustrate this definition of multiplication.

Set Model

Measurement Model

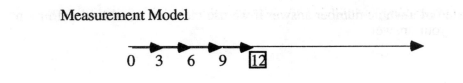

7.   Write a word problem that could be modeled by these illustrations.

Rectangular Array Approach

Often a set of similar objects may be placed in the form of a rectangular array, as depicted in the models below. For example, children sitting in a classroom, marchers in a marching band, or plants arranged in a nursery. To find the total number of objects in such an arrangement, it is easy to use the rectangular array definition of multiplication. Thus, if trees are planted in 6 rows, each of which has 10 trees, then the total number of trees is given by $6 \cdot 10 = 60$.

Set Model   Measurement Model

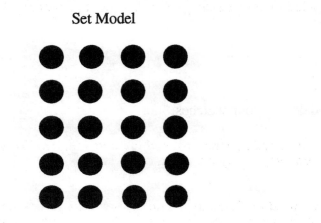

8.   Write a word problem that could be modeled by these illustrations.

Cross Product Approach

The cross product approach to multiplication can be exemplified by this problem: At a restaurant, I have 5 choices of entree, and 4 choices of dessert. In how many ways can I make my entree-dessert choice? To solve this problem, one must understand that for every choice of entree, I have 4 potential desserts to choose from.

A possible model for this perspective of multiplication is the following, also called the tree diagram model.

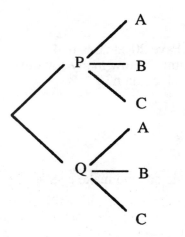

9. Write a word problem that could be modeled by the tree diagram given above, replacing P, Q, A, B, and C by your choice of objects.

Section 3.10—Division

We now come to the last of the four basic arithmetic operations, namely division. Just as with subtraction and multiplication, there are different ways of approaching division.

Sharing Approach

Here, given a certain number of objects, we need to divide them equally among a given number of sets. For example, consider the problem: If 20 pieces of candy are to be divided equally among 4 children, how many pieces of candy will each child get? To solve this problem, one would hand out pieces of candy, one at a time to each child, until one ran out of candy.

The following is a set model to illustrate this problem.

The measurement model for this problem would look similar to the multiplication measurement model. Thus, we have the following:

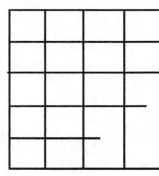

We have 20 squares in 4 columns. How many squares in each column?

10. Write a word problem using the sharing approach to division, and make a set and measurement model for it.

<u>Repeated Subtraction Approach</u>

Another way to look at division is to view it as a process of repeated subtraction. For example, suppose you have 20 pieces of candy, and you want to give 5 pieces to each child, then how many children will receive the candy? How would you solve this problem? In this case, we take away 5 pieces of candy each time and give it to a child. The process is continued until the pieces of candy are exhausted. Then we count the number of children who received 5 pieces of candy.

Viewed from this perspective, division is the reverse process of multiplication (recall that multiplication can be viewed as repeated addition). Once again, we present the set and measurement models for this view of division.

Set Model   Measurement Model

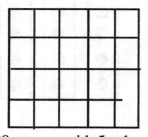

20 squares with 5 columns. How many rows?

11. Write a word problem that involves a repeated subtraction approach to division. Show the set model and measurement models for this problem.

12. Use a whole-number line model to illustrate this approach to division.

Algorithms

An algorithm is a step by step procedure that lays out in detail what you need to do to perform any task. For example, the recipes often printed on boxes of cake mixtures are algorithms for preparing the particular cake that the mixture is for. In particular, the algorithms we discuss here will be procedures that help you perform mathematical tasks. Can you think of an example of such an algorithm that you already know? Below, we will describe some of the algorithms that you will encounter in this chapter through illustrative examples.

Section 3.11—Scratch Addition Algorithm

The following algorithm is called the scratch algorithm for addition. This algorithm allows one to perform complicated additions by adding only two single digits. Each time the sum of two single digits is equal to the base or more, one records this sum by making a "scratch" line through the last digit added and writing the number of units next to the scratched digit. When a column of additions is complete, write the number of units below the addition line. Then count the number of scratch lines and add this number to the next column.

Section 3.12—Lattice Multiplication Algorithm

The following algorithm for multiplication is called the lattice multiplication algorithm. A rectangle is partitioned into a lattice with the number of rectangular regions within the large rectangle depending upon the number of digits in the factors. In the case below, the product being performed is 27 • 53 so a 2 x 2 lattice is formed with each rectangular region cut in half on the diagonal. Starting with the lower right rectangular region, the column number (7) is multiplied by the row number (3). When recording the product, the tens are written above the diagonal and the units are written below. The each column number is multiplied by each row number. When the multiplication is complete, add along the diagonals and regroup to the next diagonal if the sum of the digits exceeds the base.

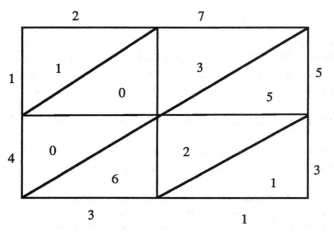

Thus, 27 x 53 = 1431.

Using Algorithm Ideas

Of course, one way in which algorithms can be used is to perform mathematical calculations. But once we understand the steps in an algorithm, we may use it to reverse the process, and instead of deducing the answer given an exercise with a set of numbers, we may use the answer to find the initial numbers. For example, we know how to add 15 and 17 to get 32. But suppose the question was to fill in the blank space in the following statement: 15 + _ = 32. What strategies would you use to answer this question? You could either subtract 15 from 32, or count off as 16, 17, ... until you reach 32. In each of these strategies, you would reverse the steps of an algorithm (and in the process create a new one) to find the answer to your question.

Bibliography

Abel, J., Allinger, G. D., & Andersen, L. (1987). "Popsicle Sticks, Computers, and Calculators: Important Considerations. *Arithmetic Teacher 34*, 8- 12.

Allinger, G D., 6: Payne, J. N. (1986). Estimation and mental arithmetic with percent. In H. L. Schoen (Ed.), Estimation and mental computation (pp. 141-155) Reston. VA: National Council of Teachers o f Mathematics

Baker, A., & Baker, J. (1991). Math's in the mind: A *process approach* to mental strategies Portsmouth. NH Heinemann.

Baroody, A. J (1985). Mastery of the basic number combinations: Internalization of relationships or facts? Journal for *Research* in Mathematics Education, 16, 83-98.

Baroody, A. J, & Standifer, D. J. (1993). Addition and subtraction in the primary grades In R. J. Jensen (Ed.), Research *ideas for* the classroom: Early childhood mathematics (pp. 72-102). Old Tappan, NJ: Macmillan.

Baroody, A. J. (1984). Children's difficulties in subtraction: Some causes and cures Arithmetic Teacher, 32(3), 14-19

Baroody, A. J., & Standifer, D. J. (1993). Addition and subtraction in the primary grades. In R J. Jensen (Ed.), Research ideas for the *classroom:* Early childhood mathematics (pp. 72-102). Old Tappan, NJ: Macmillan.

Baroody, Arthur J. "Children's Difficulties in Subtraction: Some Causes and Cures." *Arithmetic Teacher* 32 (November 1984): 14- 19. *Analyzes children's informal subtraction strategies.*

Battista, Michael T. "A Complete Model for Operations on Integers." Arithmetic Teacher 30 (May 1983): 26-31.

Beattie, lan D. "Modeling Operations and Algorithms." *Arithmetic Teacher* 33 (February 1986): 23-28.

Bobis, J. (1991). "Using a calculator to develop number sense. *Arithmetic Teacher, 38,* 42-45.

Bums, M. (1991). Introducing division through problem-solving experiences. Arithmetic Teacher, 38(8), 14-18.

Burns, M. (1989). Teaching for understanding A focus on multiplication. In P.R. Trafton (Ed.), New *directions* for elementary *school* mathematics (pp. 123-133). Reston, VA: National Council of Teachers of Mathematics.

Burns, M. (1991). Introducing division through problem solving experiences. *Arithmetic Teacher, 38,* 14- 18.

Carpenter, T. P., Carey, D. A, & Kouba, V. L. (1990). A problem-solving approach to the operations In J. N. Payne (Ed.). *Mathematics for the young child* (pp. 111-131). Reston, VA: National Council of Teachers of Mathematics.

Cemen, P. B. (1993). Teacher to teacher: Adding and subtracting integers on the number line. *Arithmetic Teacher, 40,* 388-389.

Chang, L. (1985). Multiple methods of teaching the addition and subtraction of integers. *Arithmetic Teacher, 33,* 14-19.

Clark, F. B., & Kamii, C. (1996). Identification of multiplicative thinking in children in grades 1-5. *Journal for Research in Mathematics Education, 27,* 41-51.

Corwin, R. B. (1989). Multiplication as original sin. *Journal of Mathematical Behavior, 8,* 223-225.

Crowley, M. L., & Dunn, M. L. (1985). On multiplying negative numbers. *Mathematics Teacher 78,* 252-256.

Curcio, F. R., Sicklick, F, & Turkel, S. B. (1987). Divide and conquer: Unit strips to the rescue. *Arithmetic Teacher, 35*, 6- 12.

Feinberg, M. M. (1990). Using patterns to practice basic facts. Arithmetic Teacher/(8), 38-41.

Graeber, A. O., & Tanenhaus. E. (1993). Multiplication and division: From whole-numbers to rational numbers. In D. T. Owens (Ed.), *Research ideas for the classroom: Middle grades mathematics* (pp. 99-117) Old Tappan, N]: Macmillan.

Graeber. A. O., & Baker, K. M. (1992). Little into big is the way it always is. *Arithmetic Teacher* , 39, 18-21.

Gutstein, E, & Romberg, T A. (1995). Teaching children to add and subtract. *Journal of Mathematical Behavior, 14*, 283-324.

Hall, W. D. (1983). Division with base-ten blocks. *Arithmetic Teacher* , 31, 21-23.

Hendrickson, A. D. (1986). Verbal multiplication and division problems: Some difficulties and some solutions." *Arithmetic Teacher , 33*, 26-33.

Hopkins, M. H. (1987). Number facts—or fantasy. *Arithmetic Teacher, 34*, 38-42.

Huinker, D. M (1989). Multiplication and division word problems: Improving students' understanding. *Arithmetic Teacher 37*(2), 8-12.

Kamii, C. (1994). *Young children continue to reinvent arithmetic: 3rd grade*. New York: Teachers College Press.

Kamii, C., & Joseph, L. (1988). Teaching place value and double column addition. *Arithmetic Teacher, 35*(6), 48-52.

Kamii, C., & Lewis, B. A. (1993). The harmful effects of algorithms in primary arithmetic. *Teaching K-8, 23*(5), 36-38.

Kamii, C.. Lewis, B. A., & Livingston, S. (1993). Primary arithmetic: Children inventing their own procedures. *Arithmetic Teacher, 41*, 200-203.

Kouba, V L., & Franklin, K. (1993). Multiplication and division: Sense making and meaning. In R. J. Jensen (Ed.), *Research ideas for the classroom Early childhood mathematics* (pp. 103-126). Old Tappan, NJ: Macmillan.

Lindquist, M. M. (1987). Estimation and mental computation: Measurement. *Arithmetic Teacher, 34,* 16- 18.

Lobato, J. E. (1993). Making connections with estimation. *Arithmetic Teacher, 40,* 347-351.

Mahlios, J. (1988). Word problems: Do I add or subtract? *Arithmetic Teacher, 36,* 48-52.

Meyer, Ruth A.,& James E. Riley. "Multiplication Games." *Arithmetic Teacher* 33 (April 1986): 22-25.

Pearson, E. S. (1986). Summing it all up: Pre-1900 algorithms. *Arithmetic Teacher, 33,* 38-41.

Quintero, A. H. (1986). Children's conceptual understanding of situations involving multiplication. *Arithmetic Teacher, 33*(3), 34-37.

Rathmell, E. C (1978). Teaching thinking strategies to teach the basic facts. In M. N. Suydam (Ed.), *Developing computational skills* (pp. 13-38). Reston. VA: National Council of Teachers of Teachers of Mathematics.

Rathmell, E. C., & Trafton, P. R. (1990). Whole number computation. In J. N. Payne (Ed.), *Mathematics for the young child* (pp. 153-172). Reston, VA: National Council of Teachers of Mathematics.

Remington, J. (1989). Introducing multiplication. *Arithmetic Teacher, 37,* 12- 14, 60.

Reys, B J. (1991). *Developing number sense in the middle grades: Addenda series, grades 5 - 8.* Reston, VA: National Council of Teachers of Mathematics.

Reys, B. J. & Reys, R. E. (1990). Implementing the *Standards*: Estimation—Direction from the *Standards. Arithmetic Teacher, 37,* 22-25.

Reys, R. E., & Nohda, N. (Eds.). (1993). *Computational alternatives for the twenty-first century: Cross-cultural perspectives from Japan and the United States* . Reston. VA: National Council of Teachers of Mathematics.

Rightsel, P. S., & Thornton, C. A. (1985). 72 addition facts can be mastered by mid-grade 1. *Arithmetic Teacher, 33,* 8-10.

Sowder, J. T. (1990). Mental computation and number sense. *Arithmetic Teacher, 37,* 18-20.

Stanic, G. M. A., & McKillup, W. D. (1989). Developmental algorithms have a place in elementary school mathematics instruction. *Arithmetic Teacher, 36*(5), 14-16.

Sundar, V. K. (1990). Thou shalt not divide by zero. *Arithmetic Teacher, 37,* 50-51.

Thompson, C. S., & Van de Walle, J. A. (1984). Modeling subtraction situations. *Arithmetic Teacher, 32,* 10-12.

Thompson, C. S., & Hendrickson, A. D. (1986). Verbal addition and subtraction problems: Some difficulties and some solutions. *Arithmetic Teacher, 33*(7), 21-25.

Thompson, C. S., & Hendrickson, A. D. (1986). Verbal addition and subtraction problems: Some difficulties and some solutions." *Arithmetic Teacher, 33,* 21-25.

Thompson, C. S., & Van de Walle, J. (1984). Let's do it: Modeling subtraction situations. *Arithmetic Teacher, 32,* 8-12.

Thompson, C. S., & Van de Walle, J. A. (1980). Transition boards: Moving from materials to symbols in addition. *Arithmetic Teacher, 28*(4), 4-8.

Thompson, C. S., & Van de Walle, J. A. (1981). Transition boards: Moving from materials to symbols in subtraction. *Arithmetic Teacher, 28*(5), 4-9.

Thompson, F. (1991). Two-digit addition and subtraction: What works?" *Arithmetic Teacher, 38,* 10-13.

Thornton, C A . & Toohey, M. A. (1984). A matter of facts: Addition, subtraction. multiplication, division. Palo Alto, CA: Creative Publications.

Thornton, C. A. (1990). Strategies for the basic facts. In J. N. Payne (Ed), *Mathematics for the young child* (pp. 133-151). Reston, VA: National Council of Teachers of Mathematics.

Thornton. C A. & Smith, P. (1988). Action research: Strategies for learning subtraction facts *Arithmetic Teacher, 35*(8), 9-12.

Trafton, P. R., & Zawojewski, J. S. (1990). Implementing the *Standards*: Meaning of operations. *Arithmetic Teacher, 38,* 18-22.

Tucker, B. F. (1989). Seeing addition: A diagnosis-remediation case study. *Arithmetic Teacher 36*(5), 10-11.

Van de Walle, J. A., & Thompson, C. S. (1985). Partitioning sets for number concepts, place value, and long division. *Arithmetic Teacher, 32*(5), 6-11.

Van de Walle, J. A. (1991). Redefining computation. *Arithmetic Teacher, 38*(5), 46-51.

Van Lehn, L. (1986). Arithmetic procedures are induced from examples. In J. Hiebert (Ed.), *Conceptual and procedural knowledge: The case of mathematics* (pp 133-179). Hillsdale, NJ: Erlbaum.

Weiland, L. (1985) Matching instruction to children's thinking about division. *Arithmetic Teacher, 33*(4), 34-45.

Whitin, D. J. (1994). Exploring estimation through children's literature. Arithmetic Teacher,*41,* 436-441.

Whitman, N. C. (1992). Activities: Multiplying integers. *Mathematics Teacher, 85,* 34-38, 45-51.

Chapter 4: Number Theory

Chapter Overview:

Number theory is a branch of mathematics that involves the study of numbers and, in particular, the natural numbers. In this chapter you can learn about a historical, social, and cultural context for number theory, and examine some concepts and procedures involving number theory ideas.

Big Mathematical Ideas:

conjecturing, decomposing, verifying, problem-solving strategies, and representing

NCTM Standards Links:

K - 4: Mathematics as problem solving; Mathematics as communication; Mathematics as reasoning; Mathematical connections; Number sense & numeration; Concepts of whole number operations; Patterns & relationships

5 - 8: Mathematics as problem solving; Mathematics as communication; Mathematics as reasoning; Mathematical connections; Number systems & number theory; Patterns & functions

Chapter Outline:

Historical/Social/Cultural Notes about Number Theory

Number theory, more than any other branch of mathematics, has been a field of study that has fascinated both professionals and non-professionals. Non-professionals are encouraged by the fact that, often, problems in number theory are not hard to find or understand. Besides, there are a large number of problems whose solutions do not require the development of an elaborate mathematical theory. To this extent, they are very similar to such challenging pastimes as crossword or jigsaw puzzles.

But it is also true that some of the problems that one encounters in number theory, even though easy to understand, are extremely difficult to solve and can defy the minds of the most brilliant minds. Fermat's last theorem, until recently unproved, is an example of one such problem. The theorem itself is easy to understand. It simply states that there are no non-zero whole numbers a, b, and c for which $a^n + b^n = c^n$, where n is a whole number greater than two. Can you believe that the proof of this theorem defied mathematicians for over three centuries? Other such problems that remain unsolved to this day include such results as Goldbach's conjecture, the twin prime conjecture, and Ulam's conjecture.

Some of the greatest names in the history of mathematics have also come from this area of mathematics. The German mathematician, Gauss (1777 - 1855), often called the "Prince of mathematicians," is one such example. His monumental work, the *Disquisitiones Arithmaticae*, is believed to have laid the foundations of a systematic study of the theory of numbers. Gauss wrote this work when he was only twenty! However, much of Gauss's work had to be expounded by others. Gauss once explained that he was besieged with so many ideas even before he was twenty that he only had time to write down a few of them!

Gauss's work overshadowed the work of many other (or perhaps even all—to many in the mathematics world, Gauss towers above even such giants as Newton, Euler and Hilbert) mathematicians. Other important contributors to the field of number theory include Fermat (whose theorem was mentioned above), Lagrange, Euler, Dirichlet, and Cauchy.

In modern times, one of the important number theorists has been the Indian mathematician Ramanujan (1887 - 1920). Ramanujan, working without any formal training arrived at astounding results through numerical examples and intuition. The English mathematician, Hardy, brought him to England, and became his mentor. He later remarked that he had learnt more from Ramanujan than Ramanujan had from him. Ramanujan's health, however, suffered much from neglect and the weather while in England, and he died soon after he returned to India in 1920.

Two American sisters, Julia Bowman Robinson (1919 - 1985), and Constance Bowman Reid (1917 -) have also contributed much to the field. Robinson, while working with a Russian mathematician, is credited with work that led to the solution of the tenth problem proposed by Hilbert (who suggested a set of twenty-three unsolved problems. These problems have tantalized mathematicians ever since the time that they were first suggested). Robinson was the first woman president of the American Mathematical Society.

Reid, on the other hand, is not a professional mathematician. A freelance writer, she was fascinated by number theory and has been the author of such popular books as *From Zero to Infinity*, and *A Long Way from Euclid*. Reid's latest book, *Julia: A Life in Mathematics* relates the story of Robinson's life, based on an interview conducted with her just a month before Robinson died.

Explanations Concerning Number Theory

Section 4.1—Factors and Multiples

We say a number, say a, is a *factor* of a number, say b, if a divides b evenly. This means that when you divide b by a (note the order of the numbers), the remainder is zero. Thus, 2 is a factor of 4, 8, 22, or 102, but is not a factor of 1, 5, 23, or 103. 3 is a factor of 3, 15, 75, 231, but not of 8, 16, 43, or 124. If the number a is a factor of b, we say that b is a *multiple* of a. Thus, 4, 6, 20 and 42 are multiples of 2, but 5, 23, and 63 are not multiples of 2. *Note:* Every positive number is a factor and multiple of itself.

Section 4.2—Prime and Composite Numbers

We say a number is *prime* if it has exactly two factors — 1 and itself. Examples of prime numbers include 2, 3, 17 and 29. The numbers 4, 14, 27 or 54 are not prime. A number that is not prime is said to be *composite*. Thus, a composite number will have more than two factors. Thus, the numbers 27, 32, 48 and 105 are composite. *Note:* The number 1 is the only natural number that is said to be neither prime nor composite. All other natural numbers can be categorized as either prime or composite.

One way to obtain all the primes less than a particular number is to use a method developed by the Greek mathematician Eratosthenes (276 - approximately 194 B.C.). To begin, you consider all the natural numbers less than a certain number, say 50. Then you systematically cross out the numbers that are not prime. Let us illustrate this method, called the *Sieve of Eratosthenes*, below.

We have listed the natural numbers from 1 to 50. We now start crossing out numbers that are not prime. First, we cross out 1 since it is not prime. Since 2 is prime, we do not cross out 2 (instead we will circle it to show that it is prime). However, we can now cross out every multiple of 2, since if 2 is a factor of a number greater than 2, it cannot be a prime number (why?). Since 3 is prime, we circle it, and then cross out every multiple of 3. Since 5 and 7 are prime, we circle them, and then cross out their multiples. Since 7 is the largest prime whose square (49) is less than 50, we can stop after this step and know that any numbers not crossed out are prime (why?).

$$\not{1} \quad ② \quad ③ \quad \not{4} \quad ⑤ \quad \not{6} \quad ⑦ \quad \not{8} \quad \not{9} \quad \not{10}$$

$$11 \quad \not{12} \quad 13 \quad \not{14} \quad \not{15} \quad \not{16} \quad 17 \quad \not{18} \quad 19 \quad \not{20}$$

$$\not{21} \quad \not{22} \quad 23 \quad \not{24} \quad \not{25} \quad \not{26} \quad \not{27} \quad \not{28} \quad 29 \quad \not{30}$$

$$31 \quad \not{32} \quad \not{33} \quad \not{34} \quad \not{35} \quad \not{36} \quad 37 \quad \not{38} \quad \not{39} \quad \not{40}$$

$$41 \quad \not{42} \quad 43 \quad \not{44} \quad \not{45} \quad \not{46} \quad 47 \quad \not{48} \quad \not{49} \quad \not{50}$$

Section 4.3—Prime Factorization

When one writes a composite number as a product of its prime factors, the written product is called its *prime factorization*. Thus, 2 • 3 is the prime factorization of 6, while 2 • 2 • 3 is the prime factorization of 12. Here are some more examples:

$$25 = 5 • 5, \text{ or } 5^2$$
$$48 = 2 • 2 • 2 • 2 • 3, \text{ or } 2^4 • 3$$
$$75 = 3 • 5 • 5, \text{ or } 3 \times 5^2$$

The prime factorization of a number can be written in either of the two ways shown above. In writing the prime factorization, we usually write the factors in increasing order. This is also a useful way of determining the prime factorization. Thus, to find the prime factorization of a number, find the smallest prime factor of the number, and divide the number by it. For, example, to find the prime factorization of 24, we divide by 2, which is the smallest prime factor of 24. Now, we can write 24 as 2 • 12. Now, divide 12 by its smallest prime factor, which is again 2. so, we can write 12 = 2 • 6, and 24 = 2 • 2 • 6. Now, divide 6 by its smallest prime factor, which is again 2. Continue this process until the quotient after dividing by the smallest prime is itself prime. Thus, when we divide 6 by 2 we get 3, which is prime itself. Thus, we stop here. We can now write 24 as 2 • 2 • 2 • 3, or 2^3 • 3, which is the prime factorization of 24.

Section 4.4—Even and Odd Numbers

A number is said to be *even* if it is a multiple of 2. Thus, 2, 10, 48, and 100 are all even. Numbers that are not even are said to be *odd*. Thus, 5, 13, 21, and 105 are all odd.

Section 4.5—Divisibility Tests

The numbers that we have considered so far have been small numbers. However, at some times, we may need to look at much bigger numbers to decide whether they are divisible by some smaller numbers. (Note: By saying a number b is *divisible* by a number a, we shall mean that a is a factor of b, that is, a divides b evenly.) For example, is 453836 divisible by 2? Is it divisible by 5? Is 276 divisible by 3? To find the answers to such questions quickly and without actually performing the entire division involved, we use what are called divisibility tests. Thus, a divisibility test for 2 will give you a quick and relatively easy process to find out if a given number is divisible by 2. A divisibility test for 3 will do the same for the number 3, and so on. Divisibility tests are available for several numbers such as 2, 3, 4, 5, 6, 8, 9, and 10 (there are tests for other numbers as well, but we shall restrict ourselves to these numbers in this chapter).

Here are the divisibility tests for the numbers listed above.

Divisibility Test for 2: A number is divisible by 2 if the far right digit in the number is one of 0, 2, 4, 6, or 8. For example, the numbers 2, 20, 46, 908, 24654 are all divisible by 2, since the far right digits are 2, 0, 6, 8, and 4 respectively.

Divisibility Test for 3: A number is divisible by 3 if the sum of the digits in the number is divisible by 3. For example, 24 (sum of the digits is 6), 105 (sum of the digits is 6), 29532 (sum of the digits is 21) are all divisible by 3, since the sum of the digits in each of them is divisible by 3.

Divisibility Test for 4: A number is divisible by 4 if the number formed by the two far right digits in the number is divisible by 4. For example, 348 (last two digits form the number 48), 20504 (last two digits form the number 04), and 178916 (last two digits form the number 16) are all divisible by 4, since the number formed by the last two digits of each number is divisible by 4.

Divisibility Test for 5: A number is divisible by 5 if the far right digit in the number is one of 0 or 5. For example, 25, 755, 38970, and 111135 are all divisible by 5.

Divisibility Test for 6: A number is divisible by 6 if it is divisible by both 2 and 3. For example, 48 (last digit 8 and the sum of the digits is 12), 204 (last digit 4 and the sum of the digits is 6), and 2892 (last digit 2 and the sum of the digits is 21) are all divisible by 6.

Divisibility Test for 9: A number is divisible by 9 if the sum of the digits in the number is divisible by 9. For example, 27 (sum of the digits is 9), 5967 (sum of the digits is 27), 306 (sum of the digits is 9) and 207702 (sum of the digits is 18) are all divisible by 9.

Divisibility Test for 10: A number is divisible by 10 if the far right digit in the number is 0. For example, 700, 2970, and 689270 are all divisible by 10.

Each divisibility test is based on sound mathematical principles. After you read through these tests and work through some of them in class, try and provide reasoning for each of them to understand why they work. This may also help you to devise tests for some other numbers.

Section 4.6—Greatest Common Factor

The *greatest common factor* (GCD) of two (or more) numbers is the largest number that divides both (or all) of them. For example, the greatest common factor for 16 and 28 is 4, for 27, 36 and 72 is 9, and for 26, 65 and 91 is 13. How do you find the greatest common factor of two or more numbers? Consider the example given below carefully. It will help you to work out an algorithm to find the greatest common factor of any group of numbers.

Example 1: Find the greatest common factor of 840, 1260, and 1456.

Solution: We know that

$$840 = 2^4 \cdot 3 \cdot 5 \cdot 7$$
$$1260 = 2^2 \cdot 3^2 \cdot 5 \cdot 7$$
$$1456 = 2^4 \cdot 7 \cdot 13$$

The common factors among the three numbers are 2^2 and 7. Thus, the greatest common factor of 840, 1260, and 1456 is $2^2 \cdot 7$, or 28.

Section 4.7—Least Common Multiple

The *least common multiple* (LCM) of two (or more) numbers is the smallest number that is divisible by both (or all) the numbers. For example, the least common multiple of 8, 10 and 18 is 360. Look at the following example to find an algorithm to calculate the least common multiple of a group of numbers.

Example 2: Find the least common multiple of 450, 585 and 1260.

Solution: We know that

$$450 = 2 \cdot 3^2 \cdot 5^2$$
$$585 = 3^2 \cdot 5 \cdot 13$$
$$1260 = 2^2 \cdot 3^2 \cdot 5 \cdot 7$$

Thus, the least common multiple of 675, 1260 and 1305 is $2^2 \cdot 3^2 \cdot 5^2 \cdot 7 \cdot 13 = 81900$.

Section 4.8—Modular Arithmetic

So far in this chapter, we have only looked at infinite sets of numbers. However, there are some situations in which we do arithmetic operations on finite sets of numbers. Can you think of any situations where this happens? Consider the following scenarios.

- Joan is performing an experiment with a plant. It is 10:00 a. m. now, and she must check the plant every 3 hours. What will be the next four times when she must check the plant?

- Tom met Stella today and will meet her again after 27 days on June 18. What is the date today?

The kind of arithmetic involved in the situations above is called *modular arithmetic*. For obvious reasons, it is often referred to as clock arithmetic. The process becomes more generalized when you think of clocks with time spans other than the conventional ones. Thus, we may think of 5-hour clocks, 7-hour clocks or 15-hour clocks to represent arithmetic modulo 5, arithmetic modulo 7, and arithmetic modulo 15, respectively.

Here, we will give examples of the four arithmetic operations using arithmetic modulo 7. You may find it easier to understand these operations if you can visualize them on a clock with seven digits—0, 1, 2, 3, 4, 5, and 6. You can actually represent any integer on this clock by wrapping the integer line around it. Thus, while the integers 0, 1, . . . 6 correspond to themselves, 7 will again correspond to 0, 8 to 1, 9 to 2, and so on. Similarly, –1 will correspond to 6, –2 to 5, and so on. Thus, each digit from 0 through 6 actually has an infinite number of integers associated with it. We associate a formal definition with this fact.

<u>Definition</u>: *Congruence modulo m* (or as it is often called, congruence mod m): Let a, b, and m be integers, with m ≥ 2. Then, we say a is congruent to b mod m, and write, a = b (mod m) if and only if m divides (a – b). Thus, 23 = 2 (mod 7) because 7 divides 23 – 2, or 21. Similarly, 28 = 3 (mod 5) because 5 divides 28 – 3 or 25.

We often write the number b so that it is a non-negative integer less than the number m. Thus, for congruence mod 7, b could be any one of the digits 0, 1, 2, 3, 4, 5, or 6. If we take this condition into consideration then we have the following alternative definition of congruence mod m: We say a = b (mod m) if on dividing a by m, we get the remainder b.

Thus, 25 = 4 (mod 7) because on dividing 25 by 7 we get a remainder of 4. Doing a few examples using both the definitions will help to convince you that the two definitions are equivalent.

Here are some examples in mod 7 arithmetic to illustrate the four operations. The point to remember is that the operation is performed in the usual way with the answers being written mod 7.

<u>Example 3</u>: *Addition in mod 7*
Find 5 + 3, 4 + 2, 3 + 4, and 5 + 6 in mod 7.

<u>Solution</u>: Addition mod 7 is defined as in addition with whole numbers with the answers being calculated mod 7. Since the sum of two numbers in mod 7 is the remainder of the sum divided by 7, then 5 + 3 = 1, 4 + 2 = 6, 3 + 4 = 0, and 5 + 6 = 4 in mod 7 arithmetic. In each case we simply add the numbers involved, and take the result mod 7.

<u>Example 4</u>: *Subtraction in mod 7*
Find 2 - 4, 2 - 5, and 1 - 5 in mod 7.

<u>Solution</u>: Subtraction may be viewed using the missing-addend approach. Thus, 2 – 4 = x if and only if 4 + x = 2 mod 7. Thus, x = 5 because 5 + 4 = 9, which is 2 mod 7. You may also perform subtraction by counting backwards. Thus, to subtract 4 from 2, you count back 4 units starting with 2 — 2, 1, 0, 6. Therefore, the answer will be 5. Similarly, 2 – 5 = 4, 0 – 2 = 5, and 1 – 5 = 3.

<u>Example 5</u>: *Multiplication in mod 7*
Find 4 • 6, 2 • 4, and 5 • 6 in mod 7.

<u>Solution</u>: Multiplication in mod 7 is defined as repeated addition. To find products, we may multiply two numbers as whole numbers, and calculate the answers mod 7. Thus, 4 • 6 = 3 mod 7, 2 • 4 = 1 mod 7, and 5 • 6 = 2 mod 7.

<u>Example 6</u>: *Division in mod 7*
Find 3 ÷ 4, 2 ÷ 3, 1 ÷ 4, and 5 ÷ 6 in mod 7.

<u>Solution</u>: Division in mod 7 can be viewed through the missing-factor approach. Thus, $3 \div 4 = s$ if and only if $4 \bullet s = 3$. Thus, $s = 6$ because $4 \bullet 6 = 24$, which is 3 mod 7. Similarly, $2 \div 3 = 3$, $1 \div 4 = 2$, $5 \div 6 = 2$.

Section 4.9—Proofs in Mathematics

The word "proof" in mathematics usually connotes something a little different from the same word in ordinary language. While in everyday usage, a verbal argument or visual evidence may be construed as proof of a statement, in mathematics one must often present a logically developed series of statements that irrefutably substantiate a result in order to prove it. Thereafter, the result will be accepted as proved and available for further use by mathematicians. Such proofs have a rich and long tradition in mathematics. They are often hard to develop without rigorous mathematical training, and sometimes even hard to understand!

In these course materials, we will not look at too many proofs. However, we will consider some interesting arguments for some simple results. The proofs in Chapter 4 in the *Activity Book* will be mainly visual. Thus, the intention is to construct a picture (or more often, a series of pictures) and deduce a result from them.

The following example will illustrate this idea. It shows a visual proof of the fact that the sum of the three interior angles of a triangle is 180°.

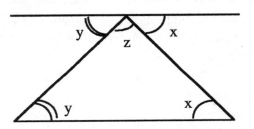

With a little bit of knowledge about alternate angles on parallel lines, one can easily see a logical, irrefutable argument in the above picture to show that the sum of the three angles of a triangle is 180°. Not all visual proofs may be as convincing as the one above. However, as long as the argument is clear and obvious from the illustration, we can regard the picture as an argument to help understand the stated fact.

Bibliography

Bezuszka, S. J. (1985). A test for divisibility by primes. *Arithmetic Teacher, 33,* 36-38.

Brown, G. W. "Searching for Patterns of Divisors." *Arithmetic Teacher* 32 (December 1984): 32-34.

Dearing, S. A. & Holtan, B. (1987). Factors and primes with a T square. *Arithmetic Teacher, 34,* 34.

Dockweiler, C. J. (1985). Palindromes and the "Law of 11." *Arithmetic Teacher , 33,* 46-47.

Graviss, T., & Greaver, J. (1992). Extending the number line to make connections with number theory. *Mathematics Teacher , 85,* 418-420.

Hudson, F. M. (1990). Are the primes really infinite? *Mathematics Teacher , 83,* 660.

Lamb, C. E., & Hutcherson, L. R. (1984). Greatest common factor and least common multiple. *Arithmetic Teacher, 31,* 43-44.

Lefton, P. (1991). Number theory and public-key cryptography. *Mathematics Teacher, 84,* 54-62.

Martinez, J. G. R. (1988). Helping students understand factors and terms. *Mathematics Teacher, 81,* 747-751.

Olson, M. (1991). Activities: A geometric look at greatest common divisor. *Mathematics Teacher, 84,* 202-208.

Chapter 5: Probability & Statistics

Chapter Overview:

A great many events in the world around us involve uncertainty and chance. It is easy to find examples from business, education, law, medicine, and everyday experience. Two examples come readily to mind: (1) the weather forecaster on TV says, "There is a 70% chance of rain tomorrow"; (2) with only a very small portion of votes counted, newscasters are able to project winners of political elections and final percentages of votes with considerable accuracy. How was the 70% figure obtained? How can newscasters attain such accuracy with so little information? The branches of mathematics called probability and statistics were developed to help us deal with situations involving uncertainty and chance in a precise and objective manner. In this chapter you can learn about a historical, social, and cultural context for probability and statistics, and examine some concepts and procedures involving probability and statistics ideas.

Big Mathematical Ideas:

Data & chance, independence/dependence, representation, mathematical model

NCTM Standards Links:

K - 4: Mathematics as problem solving; Mathematics as communication; Mathematics as reasoning; Mathematical connections; Statistics & probability

5 - 8: Mathematics as problem solving; Mathematics as communication; Mathematics as reasoning; Mathematical connections; Statistics; Probability

Chapter Outline:

Historical/Social/Cultural Notes about Probability & Statistics

Statistics

Of all the branches of mathematics, statistics is probably the most visible one in the everyday world. In fact, if you pick up any newspaper or magazine today, you are likely to come across various surveys done on different categories of population or data records such as those in sports, medicine, or the corporate world. The all-pervasive nature of statistics has made such terms as the bell curve, mean (of a set of data), sample, random sample, and bias (in a set of data) common terms in the English language. It is a different matter that often such terms are used quite loosely and their use in everyday language may not reflect their mathematical meaning.

The beginning of the modern theory of statistics and statistical analysis can be traced back to the time of the Industrial Revolution. Statistics includes the collection, organization and interpretation of data. (The mere gathering of data is not considered statistics in this sense; incidentally, data had been gathered even in biblical times.) Statistical analyses began at the time of the Industrial Revolution for some very practical reasons. It was at this time that mass production through large factories began. This created urban populations with all the attendant problems of overpopulation, disease, unemployment, and large population changes. Social scientists of that time were searching for tools to study these changes, and were unable to come to grips with the fast changing social scenario. Then, two seventeenth century Englishmen, John Graunt and William Petty, studying the death records of English cities, came across surprising patterns in these data. Based on these data, the two made some startling observations. These observations laid the foundations of the study of statistics in the modern sense. Two important early instances of the use of statistics are provided by Florence Nightingale (1820 - 1910), the famous English nurse, who worked with death records in hospitals during the Crimean war in order to show that change was desperately needed in the conditions of the hospitals, and the Austrian monk Gregor Mendel (1822 - 1911) who maintained records of his experiments, and from the results laid the foundations of the science of genetics.

One of the most common concepts that one comes across in statistics is the normal distribution curve. This curve, often called the normal curve or the Gaussian curve (after Gauss who found a large number of uses for it, and whom we encountered in Chapter 4 on number theory) occurs in a large number of real life situations. In 1833, a Belgian astronomer and statistician, Adolph Quetelet, made a startling discovery. In a study of the mental and physical traits of human beings, data on which had been gathered in large numbers by the artists of the Renaissance period, Quetelet found that almost all these traits were distributed along a normal curve. Height, the size of the brain or the head, intelligence, the sizes of different limbs were all distributed normally in any one national type. In fact, the same is true for many plant and animal groups as well. What is disturbing for modern social scientists are the data that are not normally distributed; often the records for income, higher education, and access to such facilities as proper medical care will follow skewed curves, reflecting the fact that in most societies, the benefits of prosperity are often limited to a select few.

In present times, one finds statistics being used everywhere—from pre-election polls that predict who will win the next presidential election before the election has taken place to the safest car on the road. In such a situation, one cannot but remember a remark made by the nineteenth century English prime minister, Benjamin Disraeli, who stated that "there are three kinds of lies: lies, damned lies, and statistics." He was alluding to the fact that sometimes, statistics can be used to mislead the general population. For example, suppose the chair of the mathematics department at a university claimed that in his department, the number of women employed had gone up by 100% in the last five years, would you be impressed? What if you knew that there was only one woman in a group of 45 faculty members to begin with? What if the female faculty had been hired at a fraction of the salary paid to male members of equivalent qualifications? What if the additional women had been hired as secretarial staff? These questions, whose answers are crucial to the overall situation, must be known before one can make any judgment about the employment situation in the department with regard to women. This example shows that when looking at statistical data one must be careful and alert. Without being aware of all the relevant facts, it would be only too easy to be misled by statistical data.

Notes on Probability

The study of statistics is closely related to probability in several ways. However, while the origins of the former lie in the study of social changes during the Industrial Revolution, the latter had far more dubious origins. The modern study of probability arose in the practice of gambling in the sixteenth century when the Italian physicist and mathematician Jerome Cardan, who was also a serious gambler, decided to study his chances of winning at card games. He later wrote a book, *The Book on Games of Chance*, to aid future gamblers. About a hundred years later, in France, another gambler, the Chevalier de Mere, struggled with a problem of probability. Unable to solve the problem himself, he sent it to the mathematician and his friend, Blaise Pascal. Pascal communicated this problem to his friend, Pierre de Fermat. The two French mathematicians applied themselves to this problem and remarkably, each of them solved it by different means. A steady stream of correspondence between the two about their results helped to lay the foundations of the modern theory of probability.

The study of probability is rooted in the study of such events as the tossing coins, throwing dice, and drawing cards. Pascal introduced one other interesting artifact in order to study one such event. This artifact was a triangular array of numbers that was known much before Pascal but is now named after him as Pascal's Triangle because of the ingenious use he made of this pattern. (For details on the construction of this triangle, refer to Activity 4.16.) This triangle at once gives us the probability of the different possible number of heads that may occur when any given number of coins is tossed. For example, the fourth row in the triangle reads as 1   3   3   1. The sum of these numbers is 8, which is the total number of ways in which 3 coins may be tossed. Then, 1/8 represents the probability of getting no heads among the three coins, 3/8 represents the probability of getting one heads, the next 3/8 represents the probability of getting two heads, and the final 1/8 represents the probability of getting three heads in the event. Similarly, the next row represents the probability of different events when four coins are tossed, and so on.

While the theory of probability arose in the practice of gambling, it was later applied to almost all the areas of modern social systems that are permeated by statistics, such as medicine, economics, sociology, and insurance. Perhaps the earliest, and among the most impressive, use of this theory was made by Gregor Mendel (mentioned above) in his experiments with the sweet pea plant that laid the foundations of the study of heredity and genetics. The principles founded by Mendel and known as Mendel's laws of inheritance are used widely today by people involved with the breeding and genetic studies of plants and animals.

Another interesting note on probability is added once again by Pascal, most of whose life had been quite tormented, partly because of his frail physique and partly due to his own follies. He turned towards God and religion in the last years of his life. In a practical application of his theory of probability, Pascal made a wager. The expectation in a gamble is the value of the prize multiplied by the probability of winning that prize. Pascal then stated that the value of eternal happiness is infinite. Then he reasoned that even if the probability of winning this prize by leading a religious life is extremely small, the expectation of the sample is infinite (since anything multiplied by infinity is infinity) and so it would be worthwhile to lead such a life. Pascal himself adopted such a lifestyle towards the end of his life. His theory lives on in numerous applications to all fields of human activity.

Explanations Concerning Probability & Statistics

Section 5.1—Probability of Occurrence of an Event

For any experiment to which one wishes to apply the notion of probability, it is very important to decide what possible outcomes of the experiment are of interest, and to make a list of all such outcomes. This list must be such that when the experiment is performed, exactly one of the outcomes will occur. Of course, the listing of the elements can be long and tedious. However, we can use certain counting techniques in mathematics to find the number of all desired outcomes. Let's look at an example.

Example 1: Suppose a particular family has three children. What is the probability that all three children are boys?

Solution: In this example, the first step is to find the total number of ways of having three children. The latter we call *total number of outcomes* or *sample space*. There are eight possibilities as shown in the table below.

Child #1	Child #2	Child #3
Girl	Girl	Girl
Girl	Girl	Boy
Girl	Boy	Girl
Boy	Girl	Girl
Boy	Boy	Boy
Boy	Girl	Boy
Boy	Boy	Girl
Boy	Girl	Girl

Note that only one of the outcomes yields the desired outcomes (Boy, Boy, Boy). It is customary to refer to the desired outcomes/event as *favorable outcomes*. Hence, if we let P(3 boys) denote the probability that all three children are boys, then P(3 boys) = 1/8. That is, there is 1 favorable outcome out of 8 possible outcomes.

In general, if an event can occur in n equally likely ways and if f of these ways are considered favorable outcomes, then the probability of the occurrence of the event is $p = f/n$, where $p=$ *[number of favorable outcomes]/[total number of all possible outcomes]*.

Now let's use the notion described above to complete the following example.

Example 2: Johnny does not know the answer to the first four questions on a true-false test. He decides to guess at the answers! Find the probability that he

  a. guesses all the four questions correctly
  b. guesses *at least* one of the four questions correctly
  c. misses all four questions

Solution: a. p(he guesses all 4 questions correctly) = 1/16
               b. p(he guesses at least 1 correctly) = 15/16
               c. p(he misses all 4 questions) = 1/16

Section 5.2—Fairness of Games

One thing that is of paramount importance to professional gamblers or persons who participate in state lotteries is how much money they can expect to earn in the long run by playing a particular game. Note that it is a waste of time to play a game if as much (or more) money that is earned will be lost. It is customary to refer to a game where a person has exactly the same chance of winning as losing as a *fair* game. Of course, if money can only be lost, then it is silly to play. The professional gambler will play a game if he/she knows with some certainty that some money can be earned. Mathematicians call the amount of money to be lost or won *mathematical expectation*. Consider, for instance, the following example.

Example 3: In a gambling game a man is paid $6 if he gets all heads or all tails when three coins are tossed; otherwise he pays out $4. What amount of money is he expected to earn from playing this game?

Solution: The sample space for all possible outcomes when three fair coins are tossed simultaneously, or equivalently if 1 coin is tossed three times is

$$S=\{\underline{HHH}, HHT, HTH, THH, HTT, THT, TTH, \underline{TTT}\}.$$

Each of these possibilities is equally likely and occurs with probability 1/8. Note that the man will win $6 if event E_1 = {HHH, TTT} occurs and lose $4 if event E_2 = { HHT, HTH, THH, HTT, THT, TTH}occurs.

Since E_1 and E_2 occur with probabilities 2/8 (or 1/4) and 6/8 (or 3/4) respectively, it follows that the amount of money that the man is expected to earn $6(1/4) + $(-4)(3/4) = -$1.50. (Note: $-4 represents the amount the man must pay every time he loses.)

In this game, the man will, on the average, lose $1.50 per toss of the three coins. A game is considered *fair* if the gambler will, on the average, break even. Hence, *an expected gain of zero defines a fair game*.

Section 5.3—Basic Probability Notions

The two experiments in Activity 5.5 are provided to give you more experience with basic probability notions and, in particular, to demonstrate the importance of considering whether or not replacement takes place when objects are removed in an experiment. To illustrate that the probabilities assigned to an event are different if marbles are replaced, consider the experiment involving marbles in an urn. To describe the experiment, let the 3 blue marbles be denoted as B_1, B_2, and B_3 and let the 2 orange marbles be denoted as O_1 and O_2. The sample space for this experiment is given below (Note: B_1O_2, for example, denotes drawing blue marble number 1 first, followed by orange marble 2.)

B_1B_2, B_1B_3, B_1O_1, B_1O_2, B_2B_1, B_2B_3, B_2O_1, B_2O_2, B_3B_1, B_3B_2, B_3O_1, B_3O_2, O_1B_1, O_1B_2, O_1B_3, O_1O_2, O_2B_1, O_2B_2, O_2B_3, O_2O_1.

There are 20 total outcomes and only 2 of the outcomes are 2 orange marbles (O_1O_2 and O_2O_1). So, the probability that both marbles selected are orange is 2/20 = 1/10.

Now, if after the first marble is selected (and its color recorded) it is replaced in the urn, the sample space changes—and hence the probability of selecting 2 orange marbles—as is illustrated in the sample space below:

$\mathbf{B_1B_1}$, B_1B_2, B_1B_3, B_1O_1, B_1O_2, B_2B_1, $\mathbf{B_2B_2}$, B_2B_3, B_2O_1, B_2O_2, B_3B_1, B_3B_2, $\mathbf{B_3B_3}$, B_3O_1, B_3O_2, O_1B_1, O_1B_2, O_1B_3, $\mathbf{O_1O_1}$, O_1O_2, O_2B_1, O_2B_2, O_2B_3, O_2O_1, $\mathbf{O_2O_2}$.

Notice that there are 5 new possible outcomes (namely, those involving drawing the same marble twice: B_1B_1, B_2B_2, etc.; those listed in bold in the sample space). Now the probability that both marbles selected are orange is 4/25, making the probability larger if replacement is involved.

Also included in this experiment is a question about how the probabilities might differ if an actual experiment were conducted. This question raises the issue about the distinction between *theoretical* and *experimental* (or *empirical*) probability.

Theoretical Probability refers to probability determined by analyzing an experiment or situation. If all of the outcomes have the same chance of occurring (i.e., are equally likely), the theoretical probability of an event happening can be determined by finding the ratio of the number of favorable outcomes (i.e., those you are interested in) to the total number of possible outcomes. Theoretical probability tells you what happens if an experiment is performed in the long run (i.e., if an experiment is performed a very large number of times).

Experimental Probability is one that is found by experimenting; that is, by actually performing an experiment. Experimental probabilities are used to predict what would happen over the long run. Experimental probability is also used to determine an estimate of the theoretical probability when it is not possible to make such a determination by analyzing the situation.

Section 5.4—Counting Principles

Activity 5.6, with the four situations presented, deals with four counting techniques (actually 3 techniques with one special case) used to solve what are called combinatorial problems. These techniques are commonly used to compute probabilities.

Technique I: Suppose there are m sets, the first containing n_1 elements, the second containing n_2 elements, . . . , and the *m*th set containing n_m elements. Then the number of ways to form an arrangement of *m* elements by selecting in order one element from each of the *m* sets is:

$$n_1 \bullet n_2 \bullet \ldots \bullet n_m$$

In #1.a. of Situation I, we want to find out how many different keys could be made. To use technique I to solve this problem, we notice that there are 6 sets (notch positions) and each one contains 6 elements (depth of notch position). So using technique I, we have $6 \bullet 6 \bullet 6 \bullet 6 \bullet 6 \bullet 6$ different keys.

Technique II: The number of ordered arrangements of *r* elements selected from a set with *n* distinct elements is:

$$n \bullet (n - 1) \bullet (n - 2) \bullet \ldots \bullet ([n - r] + 1)$$

Technique II is referred to as the *Principle of Permutations*.

A special case that occurs with sufficient frequency to warrant special comment is the following:

Technique IIa: The number of ordered arrangements of the elements of a set with n distinct elements is:

$$n \bullet (n - 1) \bullet (n - 2) \bullet \ldots \bullet 2 \bullet 1$$

In #1 of Situation II, we are asked to determine the number of anagrams for the letters E, N, O, and P. The problem is to find all the ordered arrangements of 4 letters. Using Technique IIa, we have $4 \bullet 3 \bullet 3 \bullet 2 \bullet 1 = 24$ arrangements.

Notice that if we had been asked to find how all the 4-letter anagrams there are if we could choose from all 26 letters of the alphabet, we would use Technique II and get: $26 \cdot 25 \cdot 24 \cdot 23 = 358,000$ arrangements (Note: In this problem, ([n - r] + 1) is ([26 - 4] + 1) = 23.

A key feature of all of the problems associated with Situation II and for which Technique II (or Technique IIa) applies is that order is important (e.g., The 4-letter anagram NOPE is different from PONE, even though the same letters are used in each.)

Technique III: The number of ways that a collection of r elements can be selected from a set of n distinct elements without regard to order is:

$$\frac{n \cdot (n - 1) \cdot (n - 2) \cdot \ldots \cdot ([n - r] + 1)}{r \cdot (r - 1) \cdot \ldots \cdot 2 \cdot 1}$$

This technique is referred to as the *Principle of Combinations*.

In problem #1 of Situation III, the collection in question is the set of 10 teams in the NCBC. Since we will select 3 teams from this set of 10, we have n = 10 and r = 3. So, using Technique III, we get:
$$\frac{10 \cdot 9 \cdot 8}{3 \cdot 2 \cdot 1} = 120 \text{ different ways that the top 3 positions can be filled.}$$

Situation IV presents a collection of problems that involve finding how many ways to do something. #1 can be solved using Technique III to obtain 35 committees. To solve #2, you might recognize a version of a problem you solved earlier in this course, but using methods other than the techniques introduced in this chapter. Technique III can be applied to give an answer of 10 matches. To solve #3, notice that order does not matter (e.g., the set {A, B, C} is the same as the set {A, C, B}), so Technique III can be used to yield 20 subsets.

To solve #4, you should notice that the situation is similar to those presented in Situation I; that is, technique I can be used. So, we have $9 \cdot 10 \cdot 26 \cdot 10 \cdot 10 \cdot 10 = 2,340,000$ different license plates.

Section 5.5—Measures of Central Tendency

Measures of central tendency, or averages, permit a statistician to summarize the data in a frequency table with a single number. The three most commonly used averages are the mean, the median, and the mode.

The *mean* of n numbers is their sum divided by n. So, we have
Mean = (sum of the n numbers) ÷ (n).

Note that there are several types of means (geometric, harmonic, and so on), but their use is specialized. We refer here to the *arithmetic mean*.

If a list of n numbers are arranged in increasing order, the *median* is the (n+1)/2 nd. Hence, when n is odd the median is the middle value in the ordered set of data, and when n is even it is the arithmetic mean of the two middle values. In other words, we can say that the *median* is the number below and above which 50% of the numbers in a distribution fall. Indeed, it is the midpoint of the distribution (also known as the 50th percentile).

It is important to observe that the median does not make use of all the numbers in a set of data. It tends to ignore the actual numerical values of extremes numbers. As a matter of fact, it is fairly common to have two very different sets of data with the same median. The following two sets of data illustrate such a case.

Set #1: 37, 65, 72, 81, 90, 93, 99

Set #2: 15, 47, 76, 81, 88, 92, 120

The median is the most appropriate average to use when *ordinal data* are involved. That is, data categorized as 1st, 2nd, 3rd, etc.

The *mode* is the most frequently occurring number in a set of data. A set of data can have more than one mode, or no mode at all when no two numbers are alike. Because the mode does not tell a statistician very much about a particular distribution it is not used very often in statistical studies.

At this point, it is plausible to ask which of the three measures of central tendency is likely to offer the best insight. One cannot be sure, for it may vary from one set of data to another. Observe, however, that the mean is the only average that makes use of all the numbers in the data. Hence, it is generally preferred over the mode and the median. However, large numbers can unduly affect the mean. On occasion, therefore, the median gives a more accurate indication of the average. To illustrate this situation, consider the following scenario.

Example 4: Suppose that the yearly salaries earned by various employees at a company are as shown in the table below. What does the average employee earn?

Name	Salary
Robinson	$10, 000
Hobson	$560, 000
Krumpe	$ 25, 000
Rodriquez	$42, 000
Smythe	$15, 000
Lewis	$12, 000

Solution: The mean of these salaries is a bit more than $110, 000. But, it would be unfair use the mean salary as a measure of what a typical employee earns. Hobson's high salary greatly impacts the arithmetic mean. To make good of the situation, the median ($20,000) would be a more appropriate average to use.

Section 5.6—Representing Unpaired Data with Box-and-Whisker Plots
The way data is organized and displayed can sometimes offer quick insight (though limited insight!) about situations under investigation. The box-and-whisker plot has proven to be useful for representing unpaired data.

To construct a box-and-whisker plot, we need to determine the *lower* and *upper quartiles* of the data, in addition to the smallest and largest value in the data set and the median (or 2nd quartile). Collectively, these measures of central tendency are referred to as the five-number summary. Suppose for instance we want to construct a box-and-whisker plot for the following data:

52, 58, 58, 70, 74, 79, 82, 83, <u>85</u>, 85, 86, 88, 88, 90, 90, 95, 96.

Note that the median of these scores is 85. Once this is done, we locate the median of the scores <u>below </u>85 and <u>above</u> 85. These are respectively 72, and 89. We refer to the numbers 72 and 89 as the *lower quartile* and *upper quartile* respectively. It is also customary to refer to the lower quartile as the *first quartile* (denoted Q_1) and to the upper quartile as the *third quartile* (denoted Q_3).

It is worth noting that the above procedure has divided our data set into 4 categories; with 4 scores in each category as illustrated below.

52 58 58 70 | 74 79 82 83 8|5 85 86 88 88 | 90 90 95 96.

To draw the box-and-whisker plots, we follow 3 steps:

1. Plot the extreme values (in this case the extreme values are 52, and 96), the median, the first quartile, and the third quartile on a *number line* as shown;

2. Build a rectangular box starting from the first quartile to the third quartiles (Note that the median divides the rectangular box into two proportions—*not necessarily equal.*)

3. Finally, draw lines segments from the extremes values to each end of the rectangular box. These segments are referred to as *whiskers*.

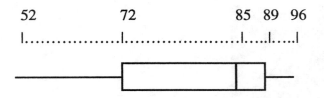

Box-and-whisker graphs can be very useful in comparing two or more sets of data.

Section 5.7—Measures of Variation

Although measures of central tendency are useful in statistics for summarizing data, they are by no means sufficient. As mentioned earlier, two set of data can have the same mean and medians, and yet be quite different. Consider for example the following two sets of data:

A: 2, 3, 25, 30, 75
B: 19, 20, 25, 32, 39

The mean in both of these distributions is 27, and the median in both is 25. Yet it is obvious that the distribution in data A is very different that that of data B.

```
x     x           x     x                                             x
           oo    o      o      o

 3  6  9  12  15    18  21  24  27    30  33  36  39    42  45  48  51    54  57  60  63    66  69  72  75    78  81  84 ...
```

These two sets of data are displayed on the number line above. Notice that the data in set A are much more spread out (i.e., more dispersed). In the statistician's view the two data differ in their *variability*. Hence, the necessity to measure such variability arises. Two commonly used measures of variation are the *range* and the *interquartile range*. The range is the difference between the maximum and minimum values in a set of data. The interquartile range is the difference between the upper or 1st quartile and the lower or 3rd quartile. This measure of variation can be useful because it represents the middle 50% of a given data set.

In addition to the range and interquartile range, statisticians use other measures of variability for more advanced work. Among these measures are the *standard deviation* and *variance*. We will not discuss them here, but if you are interested in finding out more about them consult any standard statistic book for a discussion of both of these measures.

Section 5.8—Representing Unpaired Data with Histograms

Once we have a frequency table for a set of data, we can use a *histogram* to represent the information it contains. We make a histogram by drawing two lines—one horizontal and one vertical. The range of data values—divided into equal-sized intervals— is displayed on the horizontal axis and the frequencies of those data values are displayed along the vertical line. We draw rectangles over each interval, with height of each rectangle equal to the frequency of that interval.

A graph of a frequency table obtained by drawing rectangles whose bases coincide with the intervals and whose areas are proportional to the frequencies. The sample histogram below shows the quality ratings of video tapes and the frequencies of each rating (note: ratings of this sort are often found in the magazine *Consumer Reports*.)

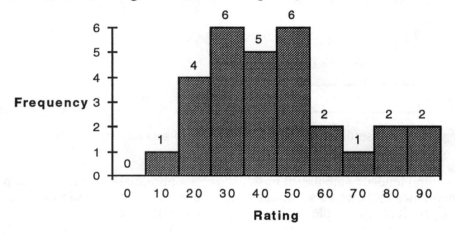

Section 5.9—Representing Paired Data with Scatter Plots

To better understand the usefulness of scatter plots, let us consider the following example.

Example 5: Suppose that we receive the scores in the table below. Furthermore, we are interested in investigating possible relationships between scores students obtain in their mathematics course and their scores in a physics course.

Name	Math Scores	Physics Scores
Julie	34	30
Bob	34	42
Andrea	36	38
Charles	46	42
Ann	49	39
Susan	54	50
Shelly	65	61
Dorothea	75	74
Sam	85	78
Hans	94	96

<u>Solution</u>: We can analyze the situation pictorially via a *scatter plot*—a pictorial representation of the relationships between two quantitative variables.

To build a scatter plot, the following requirements need to be satisfied:

1. Draw two lines—one horizontal and one vertical. (In our example, let us use the horizontal line for the math scores and the vertical line for the physics scores. Note that we could have used the vertical line for math scores. However, since we are interested in predicting the physics scores on the basis of the math scores, we deliberately use the horizontal line for the math scores.)
2. There must be a score on each variable for each student.
3. Intervals on each axis must be equal.
4. Each student must be represented by one and only one point of intersection in the graph.

The scatter plot for the above scores is shown below. Note that when the dots in the scatter plots approximate a straight line we say that there exists a *linear correlation* between the two variables (in our examples the variables are math scores and physics scores).

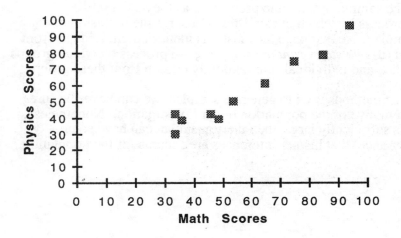

Section 5.10—Sampling

Every day we make decisions that are based on data that has been accumulated, analyzed, and interpreted. In doing so, we have reduced some of the uncertainties involved in decision making. That is what *statistics* is all about. Indeed, the primary role of statistics is to allow statisticians to draw substantial information through the analysis of data. However, such a process can be complicated at times.

Suppose, for instance, that we wish to understand how the entire US population feel about smoking in public places, we can seek the opinion of each US citizen. As you can imagine, this process is long, tedious, and above all costly. Furthermore, it may be extremely hard to absorb such a large amount of information. To make good of the situation, the statistician would select a small group or sample of the population that he/she wishes to investigate. From the selected sample inferences about the population will be made.

When a sample is representative, all the characteristics of the population are assumed to be present in the sample in the same degree. If the sample is representative, then the statistician is entitled to assume that his/her findings are also true of the population. Hence, the question how to draw samples so that valid inferences concerning a particular population can be made is of paramount importance for the statistician.

There exists no specific procedure that can guarantee samples that are representative of a population. However, statisticians prefer *random sampling* because it is likely to generate samples that are representative of the population being studied. Then it may be important for the statistician to make probabilistic statements about the "closeness" of the characteristics of the sample or samples to those of the population.

Random sampling is a procedure in which every member of the population has the same chance of being selected. In terms of probability this implies that the probability of any particular member being selected is 1/N, where N is the number of individuals in the population. More generally, if the samples is to contain R individuals, in which case the sample is said to be of size R, the sampling is random if and only if every combination or R individuals has the same probability of being chosen. Observe that the larger a random sample is in size, the more likely it is to be representative of the population.

There are several sophisticated ways of generating random sample. We shall not worry about these ways for the scope of this book. These include: (a) the use of a *table of random numbers*— a very long list of random numbers that has no order or pattern (this list can usually be found in books of statistics), (b) the use of *stratified random sampling*—a process by which certain subgroups, or *strata*, are chosen for the sample in the same proportion as they exist in the population, (c) *cluster sampling*—a process by which the statistician insures the inclusion of certain kinds of individuals in the sample (note that once the cluster is identified, individuals from the cluster are chosen randomly), and (d) *two stage-random sampling*—a process by which groups from a population are randomly selected and individuals are randomly chosen from these groups.

It is worth noting that no matter the methods used to generate samples, we can never be sure that the chosen sample will be representative of the population under investigation. Nonetheless, if the sample is randomly chosen, and is sufficiently large, then the statistician can have some assurance (though never absolute assurance) that his/her inferences are accurate of the population.

Bibliography

Armstrong, R. D. (1981). An area model for solving probability problems. In A. P. Shulte (Ed.), Teaching statistics and probability (pp. 135-142). Reston, VA: National Council of Teachers of Mathematics.

Bright, G W., Harvey, J. G., & Wheeler, F. (1981). Fair games. Unfair games. In A. P. Shulte (Ed.), *Teaching statistics and probability* (pp. 49-59). Reston, VA: National Council of Teachers of Mathematics.

Bruni, J. V., & Silverman, H. J. (1986). Developing concepts in probability and statistics—and much more. *Arithmetic Teacher, 33*(6), 34-37.

Bryan, E. H. (1988). Exploring data with box plots. *Mathematics Teacher, 81*, 658-663.

Burrill, G., Burrill, J. C., Coffield, P., Davis, G., de Lange, J., Resnick, D., & Siegel, M. (1992). *Data analysis and statistics across the curriculum: Addenda series, grades 9-12*. Reston, VA: National Council of Teachers of Mathematics.

Corwin, R. B., & Friel, S. N. (1990). *Statistics: Prediction and sampling.* (A unit of study for grades 5-6 from Used numbers: Real data in the *classroom.)* Palo Alto, CA: Dale Seymour.

Dessart, D. J. (1995). Randomness: A connection to reality. In P. A. House (Ed.), *Connecting mathematics across the curriculum* (pp. 177-181). Reston, VA: National Council of Teachers of Mathematics.

Dickinson, J. C. (1986). Gather, organize, display: Mathematics for the information society." *Arithmetic Teacher, 34*, 12- 15.

Drake, B. M. (1993). Sharing teaching ideas: Exploring "different" dice. *Mathematics Teacher, 86*, 380-382.

English, L. (1992). Problem solving with combinations. *Arithmetic Teacher 40* , 72-77.

Fennel, Francis (Skip). "Implementing the Standards: Probability.' *Arithmetic Teacher* 38 (December 1990): 18-22.

Freud, E. J. (1993). *Introduction to Probability.* New York: Dover.

Friel, S. N., Mokros, J. R., & Russell, S. J. (1992). *Middles, means, and in-between.* (A unit of study for grades 5 - from Used numbers: Real data in the classroom.) Palo Alto, CA: Dale Seymour.

Friel, Susan H., and Rebecca B. Corwin. "Implementing the Standards: The Statistics Standards in *K-8* Mathematics.- Arithmetic Teacher 38* (October 1990): *35-39.*

Goldman, P. H. (1990). Teaching arithmetic averaging: An activity approach. *Arithmetic Teacher, 37*(7), 38-43.

Hatfield, L. L. (1992). Activities: Explorations with chance. *Mathematics Teacher , 85*, 280-282, 288-290.

Hinders, D. C. (1990). Examples of the use of statistics in society. *Mathematics Teacher, 83,136- 141.*

Hollingdale, S. (1994). *Makers of Mathematics.* New York: Penguin Books.

Horak, V. M. & Horak, W. J. (1983). "Let's do it: Take a chance." *Arithmetic Teacher, 30*, 8- 15.

Huff, W. D. (1954). *How to lie with statistics.* New York: Norton.

Jones, K. S. (1993). The birthday problem again. *Mathematics Teacher, 86*, 373-377.

Landwehr, J. M., & Watkins, A. E. (1987). *Exploring data: Quantitative literacy series.* Palo Alto, CA: Dale Seymour.

Leutzinger, L. P. (1990). Graphical representation and probability. In J. N. Payne (Ed.), *Mathematics for the young child* (pp. 251-263). Reston, VA: National Council of Teachers of Mathematics.

Lindquist, M. M. (1992). *Making sense of data: Addenda series, grades K-6*. Reston, VA: National Council of Teachers of Mathematics.

Manin, H. M., & Zawojewski, J. S. (1993). Dealing with data and chance: An illustration from the middle school addendum to the standards. *Arithmetic Teacher, 41,* 220-223.

May, E. Lee, Jr. (1992). Are seven-game baseball playoffs fairer? *Mathematics Teacher, 85,* 528-531.

National Council of Teachers of Mathematics. (1990). Data analysis: Minifocus issue. *Mathematics Teacher, 83*(2).

Newman, C. M., Obremski, T. E., & Schaeffer, R. L. (1987). *Exploring probability: Quantitative literacy series.* Palo Alto, CA: Dale Seymour.

Orkin, M. (1996). *Can you win?: The real odds for casino gambling, Sport betting, and lotteries.* New York: Freeman.

Parker, J., & Widmer, C. C. (1992). Teaching mathematics with technology: Statistics and graphing. *Arithmetic Teacher, 39,* 48-52.

Paull, S. (1990). Not just an average unit. *Arithmetic Teacher, 38, 54-58.*

Phillips, E., Lappan, G., Winter, M J., & Fitzgerald, W. (1986). *Middle grades mathematics project: Probability.* Menlo Park, CA: Addison-Wesley.

Porter, M. T. (1986). *The Rise of Statistical Thinking 1820- 1900.* Princeton, NJ: Princeton University Press.

Richbart, L., & Richbart,C. (1992). Trading Alfs for a Bart: A simulation." *Arithmetic Teacher, 40,* 112- 114.

Russell, S. J., & Corwin, R. B. (1989). *Statistics: The shape of the data.* (A unit of study for grades 4-6 from *Used numbers: Real data in the classroom.)* Palo Alto, CA: Dale Seymour.

Russell, S. J., & Friel, S. N. (1989). Collecting and analyzing real data in the elementary classroom. In P. R. Trafton (Ed.), *New directions for elementary school mathematics* (pp. 134-148) . Reston, VA: National Council of Teachers of Mathematics.

Schule, H. S., & Leonard, B. (1989). Probability and intuition. *Mathematics Teacher, 82,* 52-53.

Schwartzman, S. (1993). An unexpected expected value. *Mathematics Teacher, 86,* 118- 120.

Shaughnessy, J. M. (1993). Connecting research to teaching: Probability and statistics. *Mathematics Teacher, 86,* 244-248.

Shaughnessy, J. M., & Dick, T. (1991). Monty's dilemma: Should you stick or switch? *Mathematics Teacher, 84,* 252-256.

Shulte, A. P. (1987). Research report: Learning probability concepts in elementary school mathematics. *Arithmetic Teacher, 34,* 32-33.

Shulte, A. P. (Ed.). (1981). *Teaching statistics and probability* Reston, VA: National Council of Teachers of Mathematics.

Shulte, A. P. & Smart, J. R. (Eds.). (1981). *Teaching statistics and probability* (1981 yearbook of the National Council of Teachers of Mathematics). Reston, VA: NCTM.

Stevens, J. (1993). Generating and analyzing data. *Mathematics Teacher, 86,* 475-478, 487-489.

Uccellini, J. C. (1996). Teaching the mean meaningfully. *Mathematics Teaching in the Middle Grades, 2,* 112-115.

Used numbers: Real data in the classroom. Palo Alto. CA: Dale Seymour.

Von Mises, R. (1981). *Probability, Statistics, and Truth.* New York: Dover.

Weaver, W. (1963). *Lady luck.* New York: Dover Publications.

Zawojewski, J. (1992). Dealing with data and *chance: Addenda series, grades 5-8.* Reston, VA: National Council of Teachers of Mathematics.

Chapter 6: Fraction Models & Operations

Chapter Overview:

Many real-world situations require the use of fractions. It is important for anyone who will teach fraction concepts and procedures to children to have a deep understanding of fractions models and operations. In this chapter you can learn about a historical, social, and cultural context for fractions, and examine some concepts and procedures involving fraction ideas.

Big Mathematical Ideas:

problem-solving strategies, conjecturing, verifying, decomposing, generalizing, using language & symbolism, mathematical structure

NCTM Standards Links:

K - 4:   Mathematics as problem solving; Mathematics as communication; Mathematics as reasoning; Mathematical connections; Number sense and numeration; Fractions & decimals

5 - 8:   Mathematics as problem solving; Mathematics as communication; Mathematics as reasoning; Mathematical connections; Number & number relationships

Chapter Outline:

Historical/Social/Cultural Notes about Fractions

The word "fraction" is commonly used today to denote some part of a whole. The idea of fractions and the present symbol for writing a fraction as two integers placed one over the other with a bar in between them, however, took a long time to develop in its present form. The word "fraction" itself comes from a Latin word, which means "to break." The Babylonians, who used a sexagesimal system of numeration commonly used fractions that had 60 or powers of 60 in the denominator. The system is now useful in expressing measures of time or angles.

The earliest accounts of the use of fractional quantities on a wide and practical scale come from Egypt (about 1600 B.C.), where they appeared on a roll of leather that dates back to the same time as the Ahmes Papyrus, the most important source of our knowledge of Egyptian mathematics. The roll of leather is a mathematical table that consists of decompositions of fractions into unit fractions. Unit fractions are fractions that have 1 in the numerator. The Egyptians expressed all ratios as unit fractions, decomposing all other fractions into them, and developing elaborate tables that listed such decompositions.

Egyptian fractions appear in the form of hieroglyphics (pictorial symbols for numerals which we discussed in the chapter on numeration) representing unit fractions. For example, we have the following unit fractions written as hieroglyphics,

$$\frac{1}{3} = \bigcirc\ |\,|\,| \qquad \frac{1}{12} = \bigcirc\ |\,| \qquad \frac{1}{21} = \bigcirc\ |$$

The Egyptians used fractions for very practical purposes. They did not have a monetary system, and trade was based on a barter system of exchange of goods. This probably led them into developing a system of operations with fractions. While the Egyptians did not work with the modern techniques of operations of fractions, their rather complex system of such operations worked remarkably well with them.

Later, fractions appear in the work of the Hindu mathematician, Brahmagupta, who lived around A.D. 628. The Hindus wrote fractions by placing integers one on top of another, without a line between them. Compound fractions, such as (1 1/3 were written as three integers being placed one on top of the other. The Arabs are credited with the present way of writing down a fraction with a bar placed between the two integers. Sources from these two civilizations show that both of them knew how to divide a fraction by another by inverting the divisor. The techniques somehow mysteriously disappeared until the seventeen century but thereafter has come to stay as a useful tool in operations with fractions.

Various texts written during the times of the early civilizations such as the ones mentioned above contain interesting problems. Here is one about the life of Diophantus, the Greek mathematician who made important contributions to algebra. Little is known about him except his age at death, which has been preserved in the riddle below. See if you can solve it.

Diophantus' youth lasted 1/6 of his life. He grew a beard after 1/12 more. After 1/7 more of his life he married. Five years later he had a son. His son lived exactly 1/2 as long as his father. Diophantus died just 4 years afterwards. How old was Diophantus when he died?

(Answer: 84 years)

Explanations Concerning Fractions

Section 6.1—Fractions and Rational Numbers

A fraction is a number of the form a/b, where a and b are any numbers, and b ≠ 0. We note that the numbers a and b are not necessarily integers. For example, 2/3, 7/4, –7/9, and √3/5 are all fractions.

A rational number is a number of the form a/b, where a and b are any integers, and b ≠ 0. For example, 2/3, –5/4, and 25/47 are rational numbers. In a rational number, we refer to the number on top (or to the left of the bar) as the numerator, and the number below (or to the right of the bar) as the denominator. Thus, in the examples given, 2, –5, and 25 are numerators, and 3, 4, and 47 are denominators.

As we can see from the definitions, the set of rational numbers is a subset of the set of fractions. In this chapter, however, we shall use the term "fractions" to refer to rational numbers.

Fractions are used in different ways in the real world. We often come across such terms as half a chocolate, or one fourth of a pizza, or one third of a length. In such examples, we are using fractions to refer to a certain part of a whole. The whole object then denotes a unit that can be divided into fractional parts. But, sometimes, we also talk about such fractions as half the boys in a class, or one third of a person's salary. In these cases, we take the total number of boys, or the total salary, in dollars to be one unit. Thus, if there are 20 boys in a class, half the boys refers to 10 of them, or half the total number. Similarly, if a person's annual salary is $ 45,000, then one-third of the salary is $ 15,000. Fractions are also used to express ratios, as in one table for every three chairs in a room means that the table and chairs are in the ratio of 1:3.

Section 6.2—Equivalent Fractions

Consider each of the following series of pictures

a.

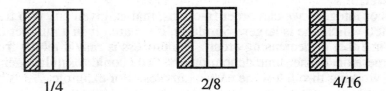

b.

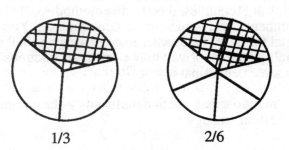

In the series of pictures in a., the shaded area in all the three pictures in that series is the same. However, in the first picture in the series, the total area is divided into four parts, so that the shaded area can be written as 1/4; in the second picture, the total area is divided into eight parts, so that the shaded area is written as 2/8; in the third picture, the total area is divided into 16 parts, and the shaded area is then written as 4/16. Thus, we see that the same part of a whole can be represented by different looking fractions. We resolve this difficulty by saying that the different fractions in (a), that is 1/4, 2/8, and 4/16 are all equivalent.

Similarly in the two pictures in b., the same area of the circle has been shaded, but different fractions represent this area. Thus, the two fractions are equivalent.

The fractions in each of the following series are equivalent.
a. 1/2, 4/8, 22/44, 13/26 (all equivalent to 1/2).
b. 2/3, 6/9, –14/–21, 10/15 (all equivalent to 2/3)
c. –2/5, 2/–5, –8/20, 6/–15 (all equivalent to –2/5).

While we may write fractions with negative denominators, conventionally the negative sign is placed in the numerator.

Section 6.3—Fractions in Simplest Terms
A fraction is said to be in its simplest terms if the numerator and denominator do not share a common factor. Thus, 2/3, 1/5, and 17/23 are in their simplest terms. However, 4/6, –5/15, and –4/–5 are not in their simplest terms.

<u>Example 1</u>: Fill in the blanks in each of the following cases:
a.   5/7 = ___ /35   b.   8/13 = 64/____   c.   4/11 = 12/ ____   d.   9/5 = ___ /100

<u>Solution</u>: a. 25   b. 104   c. 33   d. 180

<u>Example 2</u>: Write the following fractions in their simplest terms.
a. 24/72   b. 35/91   c. 121/88   d. 36/72   e. 48/6

<u>Solution</u>:   a. 1/3   b. 5/13   c. 11/8   d. 1/2   e. 8

Section 6.4—Ordering Fractions
Just as with whole numbers or integers, we can order fractions, that is, given any two fractions that are not equivalent, we can tell which one is larger. Similarly, if we are given a number of fractions, we can arrange them in either or decreasing order. The process is easy if all the fractions to be ordered have the same numerators or the same denominators. You could formulate general rules to order such fractions by working through some easy examples. For example, 2/3 is bigger than 1/3 and 5/11 is smaller than 5/9.

There are different methods one may adopt to decide which of two fractions is smaller or larger. You may draw models such as strips or rectangles, though this method would become cumbersome if the fractions have large numbers in the numerator or denominator. You may convert the fractions into equivalent decimal forms that are easier to compare (we shall discuss this in more detail later), you may use cross multiplication, or you may convert all fractions to equivalent fractions, all of which have the same denominator.

We shall discuss two of the procedures mentioned above in detail here — the common denominator strategy and the cross multiplication strategy.

The Common Denominator Method
As we said earlier, fractions become easier to compare if they have the same denominator (or the same numerator—conventionally, the denominator is used for this purpose). It is this reasoning that we use as a basis for this method. The process itself is quite simple. Given a number of fractions that are to be ordered in increasing or decreasing succession, we convert each of the fractions into an equivalent fraction so that each of them has the same denominator. Then, the fractions can be ordered by merely looking at the numerators in all the fractions. The common

denominator chosen for this purpose is usually the least common multiple (discussed in Chapter 4) of the denominators. Once the fractions have been ordered, we may convert the fractions back to their original form.

Here are two examples that will illustrate the algorithm to be followed.

Example 3: Arrange the fractions 7/5, 2/3, 5/6, and 11/10 in decreasing order.

Solution: Step 1: We look for a common denominator for all the fractions. Thus, we shall look for the least common multiple of 5, 3, 6, and 10, which is 30.

Step 2: Convert all the fractions to equivalent fractions that have the denominator 30. Thus, 7/5 = 42/30 (To get this fraction, divide 30 by 5. This gives us 6. Now, multiply 7 by 6, which is 42. thus, the equivalent fraction is 42/30). Similarly, 2/3 = 20/30; 5/6 = 25/30, 11/10 = 33/30.

Step 3: Thus, instead of the original fractions we are now comparing 42/30, 20/30, 25/30, and 33/30. We can now work out the order by looking only at the numerators. Thus, the order of the fractions is 20/30, 25/30, 33/30, and 42/30.

Step 4: We convert back to the original fractions. Thus, the order is 2/3, 5/6, 11/10, and 7/5.

Example 4: Arrange the fractions 2/3, 5/6, 1 3/5, 4/5, and 4/9, 15/9 in increasing order.

Solution: Step 1: We first convert all mixed fractions into improper ones. Thus, 1 3/5 is written as 8/5.

Step 2: We need to find a common denominator. Thus, we will look for the least common multiple of 3, 5, 6, and 9, which is 90.

Step 3: Convert all the fractions to equivalent fractions such that the denominator in each case is 90.

Thus, 2/3 = 60/90 (To get this fraction, we first divide 90 by 3. This gives us 30. Now, multiply 2 by 30. This gives us 60. Hence, the equivalent fraction is 60/90).

Similarly, 5/6 = 75/90; 1 3/5 = 8/5 = 144/90; 4/5 = 72/90; 4/9 = 40/90; 15/9 = 150/90. So, now instead of the fractions given originally, we will compare 60/90, 75/90, 144/90, 72/90, 40/90, and 150/90.

Step 4: We now need to compare only the numerators. Thus, the fractions in the increasing order are 40/90, 60/90, 72/90, 75/90, 144/90, and 150/90.

Returning to the original fractions, we have the following order: 4/9, 2/3, 4/5, 5/6, 1 3/5, and 15/9.

The Cross-Multiplication Method

This method is useful in comparing two fractions. We can use the method successively if there are more fractions involved. This method involves the following procedure. Suppose we want to compare the fractions a/b and c/d. We form the cross products ad and bc. Now, if ad > bc, then a/b > c/d, and vice versa.

Example 5: Which fraction is larger: 5/6 or 7/9?

<u>Solution</u>: We form the cross products 5 • 9 = 45, and 7 • 6 = 42. Since 5 • 9 is greater than 7 • 6, thus, 5/6 > 7/9.

<u>Example 7</u>: Arrange the following fractions in increasing order
   (a) 3/7, 21/5, 13/14, 19/4, 17/20
   (b) 8/3, 5/9, 8/15. 6/5, 7/10

<u>Solution</u>: (a) 17/20, 3/7, 13/14, 21/5, 19/4   (b) 8/15, 5/9, 7/10, 6/5, 8/3

Section 6.5—Operations With Fractions
   Just like with whole numbers and integers, we can perform all four mathematical operations with fractions. We will describe the processes for each of these operations and illustrate the procedures with examples in this section.

<u>Addition and Subtraction With Fractions</u>
   We take up these two operations together as the procedure for both of them is quite similar. As with the process of ordering fractions, it is easier to add and subtract fractions when they have the same denominators. In such a situation, we merely have to operate with the numerators. Thus, the sum of two fractions with the same denominator is the sum of the numerators of the two fractions over the common denominator. Thus, 4/7 + 2/7 = (4 + 2)/7 = 6/7. Similarly, to subtract a fraction from another with the same denominator, we subtract its numerator from the numerator of the other fraction (from which we are subtracting), and place the difference over the same denominator. Thus, 4/7 − 2/7 = (4 − 2)/7 = 2/7.

   As you may guess, we will now use the same principle to add and subtract fractions that we did to order them, namely, convert all the fractions involved into equivalent fractions with the same denominator. Thus, to add two or more fractions, we will convert them into fractions with the same denominator, and then follow the same procedure that we outlined above. We shall do the same to subtract one fraction from another. We illustrate these processes through examples.

<u>Example 8</u>: Find the sum of 4/5 and 2/7.

<u>Solution</u>: We convert both the fractions to get equivalent fractions with the same denominator. the common denominator in this case is 35 — the least common multiple of 5 and 7.

Then, we can write 4/5 = 28/35, and 2/7 = 10/35.
Thus, 4/5 + 2/7 = 28/35 + 10/35 = 38/35.

In this case, the answer, 38/35 is in its simplest terms, but if it is not then we need to convert it to its simplest terms.

<u>Example 9</u>: Find 7/9 − 3/5.

<u>Solution</u>: We convert 7/9 and 3/5 to equivalent fractions with a common denominator. In this case, the common denominator will be 45. Thus, 7/9 = 35/45, and 3/5 = 27/45.
So, we get, 7/9 − 3/5 = (35 − 27)/45 = 8/45.

<u>Example 10</u>: Perform the following operations and write the answers in the simplest terms
    (a) 3/5 + 5/3 + 7/9
    (b) 5/12 + 11/36 + 1/2
    (c) 9/11 – 1/6
    (d) 1/2 – 5/7
    (e) 1 + 11/6 + 5/8
    (f) 5 – 9/4
    (g) (2 + 1/5) – (1/3 + 1/5)
    (h) 3 1/4 – 2 1/5

<u>Solution</u>: (a) 137/45 (b) 11/9 (c) 43/66 (d) –3/14 (e) 3 11/24 (f) 11/4 (g) 5/3 (h) 1 1/20

Multiplication with Fractions

The multiplication of fractions is slightly more complicated than the addition or subtraction of fractions. Here, we view multiplication of two fractions as taking a part of another part. For example, we view 2/3 • 1/2 as taking two-thirds of a half. In effect, this means we take an object, divide it into two equal parts, and then take two-thirds of one of the parts. This process is illustrated below.

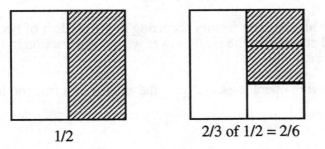

1/2   2/3 of 1/2 = 2/6

From the above illustration, we see that 1/2 • 2/3 = 2/6. This fraction may of course be written in its simplest terms as 1/3.

Thus, to multiply two fractions, we take the product of the numerators and place it over the product of the denominators. This process works in the same way even if one of the numbers in the product is an integer. Thus, 3 • 3/7 = 9/7, –2 • 5/3 = –10/3, –1/2 • – 3 = 3/2.

Division of Fractions

To perform division with fractions, we once again appeal to the common denominator strategy. Consider the following division operation: 9/11 ÷ 3/11. Modeling this operation after whole number division, we see that this is the same as asking how many three-elevenths are there in nine-elevenths. Consider the models of the two fractions below.

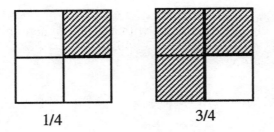

1/4   3/4

Looking at the models, we can see that there are three one-fourths in three-fourths. Thus, it becomes easy to answer questions such as 8/9 ÷ 2/9 (= 4), 15/4 ÷ 3/4 (= 5), and so on. We now come to a more difficult proposition: what is 3/5 ÷ 2/5? Once again, we interpret this question as: how many two-fifths in three-fifths? Consider the following models for the two fractions.

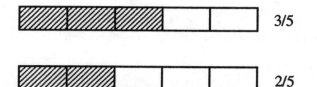

3/5

2/5

Looking at this model, we can see there are one and a half two-fifths in three-fifths. (If it is hard to see this, consider superimposing the strip that shows 2/5 on the strip that shows 3/5. Consider the two shaded rectangles of 2/5 as one unit. Then, you will have to place one and a half such units on the 3/5 strip to cover the shaded rectangles there). Thus, 3/5 ÷ 2/5 = 1 1/2 = 3/2.

By modeling several such fractions, we see the pattern as follows. To divide a fraction a/b by another fraction c/d, we invert the fraction c/d, and multiply the result with a/b. Thus, 5/7 ÷ 1/2 = 5/7 • 2/1 = 10/7, 4/9 ÷ 3/5 = 4/9 • 5/3 = 20/27, and 4/7 • 8/3 = 4/7 • 3/8 = 3/14.

Note: It is easier to remove all common factors occurring in the product of two numbers before we actually multiply. This will ensure that the final answer we get is a fraction in its simplest terms. We did this with the last example.

Example 11: Perform the following operations, and give the answer as a fraction in its simplest terms.
    (a) 4/3 • 6/7 • 5/8
    (b) 5/14 • 7/15 • 7/8
    (c) 3/4 ÷ 3/8
    (d) 5/7 ÷ 8/13
    (e) (5/4 • 12/35 • 7/50) ÷ 2/3
    (f) 3/5 • 4/7 • 35/12
    (g) (17/14 ÷ 34/35) • 2/3
    (h) 1/9 • 9/13 • 91/105

Solution: (a) 5/7 (b) 7/48 (c) 2 (d) 65/56 (e) 9/100 (f) 1 (g) 5/6 (h) 1/15

Bibliography

Behr, M. J., Post, T. R., & Wachsmuth, 1. (1986). Estimation and children s concept of rational number size. In H. L. Schoen (Ed.), *Estimation and mental computation* (pp.103-111). Reston, VA: National Council of Teachers of Mathematics.

Bezuk, N. S. (1988). Fractions in the early childhood mathematics curriculum. *Arithmetic Teacher, 35,* 56-60.

Bezuk, N. S., & Bieck, M. (1993). Current research on rational numbers and common fractions: Summar), and implications for teachers. In D. T. Owens (Ed.*), Research ideas for the classroom:Middle grades mathematics* (pp. 118-136) Old Tappan, NJ; Macmillan.

Bezuk, N. S., & Cramer, K. (1989). Teaching about fractions: What, when, and how? In P R. Trafton (Ed.), *New directions for elementary school mathematics* (pp 156-161) Reston, VA: National Council of Teachers of Mathematics.

Cramer, K., & Bezuk, N. (1991). "Multiplication of fractions: Teaching for understanding. *Arithmetic Teacher, 39,* 34-37.

Dorgan, K. (1994). What textbooks offer for instruction in fraction concepts. *Teaching Children Mathematics, 1,* 150-155.

Edge, D. (1987). Fractions and panes. *Arithmetic Teacher, 34,* 13-17.

Ettline, J. F. (1985). A uniform approach to fractions. *Arithmetic Teacher, 32,* 42-43.

Greenwood, J. (1989). Problem solving with fractions. *Mathematics Teacher, 82,* 44-50.

Hollis, L. Y. (1984). Teaching rational numbers—Primary grades. *Arithmetic Teacher, 31,* 36-39.

Howard, A. C. (1991). Addition of fractions: The unrecognized problem. *Mathematics Teacher, 84,* 710-713.

Kieren, T. E. (1984). Helping children understand rational numbers. *Arithmetic Teacher, 31,* 3.

Kieren, T., Davis, B., & Mason, R. (1996). Fraction flags Learning from children to help children ream. *Mathematics Teaching in the Middle School, 2,* 14-19.

Lester, F. K. (1984). Preparing teachers to teach rational numbers. *Arithmetic Teacher 31,* 54-56.

Mack, N. K. (1993). Making connections to understand fractions. *Arithmetic Teacher, 40,* 362-364.

Ockenga, E. (1984). Chalk up some calculator activities for rational numbers. *Arithmetic Teacher, 31, 51-53.*

Ott. J. M., Snook, D. L., & Gibson, D. L. (1991). Understanding partitive division of fractions. *Arithmetic Teacher, 39,* 7-11.

Post, T. R. & Cramer, K. (1987). Children's strategies in ordering rational numbers. *Arithmetic Teacher, 35,* 33-35.

Pothier, Y. & Sawada, D. (1990). Partitioning: An approach to fractions. *Arithmetic Teacher, 38,* 12- 16.

Sinicrope, R. & Mick, H. W. (1992). Multiplication of fractions through paper folding. *Arithmetic Teacher, 40,* 116- 121.

Skypek, D. H. B. (1984). Special characteristics of rational numbers. *Arithmetic Teacher, 31,* 10-12.

Steffe, L. P. & Olive, J. (1991). Research into practice: The problem of fractions in the elementary school. *Arithmetic Teacher, 38,* 22-24.

Trafton, P. R., & Zawojewski, J. S. (1984) Teaching rational number division: A special problem. *Arithmetic Teacher, 31*(6), 20-22.

Witherspoon, M. L. (1993). Fractions: In search of meaning. Arithmetic *Teacher, 10*, 482-485.

Chapter 7: Real Numbers: Rationals & Irrationals

Chapter Overview:

As technology (especially calculators) becomes more and more prevalent for everyday use, as well as for scientific purposes, so does the use of decimals (and percent). At the same time, ratio and proportion are also quite useful to solve a variety of real-world problems. In this chapter you can learn about a historical, social, and cultural context for rational and irrational numbers, and examine some concepts and procedures involving real number ideas.

Big Mathematical Ideas:

problem-solving strategies, conjecturing, verifying, decomposing, generalizing, representation, using language & symbolism, limit, mathematical structure

NCTM Standards Links:

K- 4 : Mathematics as problem solving; Mathematics as communication; Mathematics as reasoning; Mathematical connections; Fractions & decimals

5 - 8: Mathematics as problem solving; Mathematics as communication; Mathematics as reasoning; Mathematical connections; Number & number relationships

Chapter Outline:

Historical/Social/Cultural Notes about Rationals & Irrationals
Explanations Concerning Rationals & Irrationals

Historical/Social/Cultural Notes about Rational and Irrational Numbers

As mentioned in Chapter 6, there is documented evidence to show that several ancient civilizations knew about and used numbers of the form p/q (where p and q are integers, and q ≠ 0) in their calculations. Such numbers came to be known as rational numbers, and were used widely by people not only in mathematics but in ordinary life.

The discovery of the irrational numbers (that is, numbers that cannot be expressed in the form described for rational numbers), however, was marked by a great deal of secrecy. The Pythagoreans, who first discovered such numbers, were unable to accept their existence. The Pythagoreans were a society of Greek scholars that was started by Pythagoras (570 B.C.). The society, devoted to scholarship in various areas, became very secretive in later years. In fact, it is believed that Hippasus, one of their members, was drowned after he shared the secret of such numbers with an outsider! By 300 B.C., many irrational numbers were known. Examples of such numbers include √2, √3, and √6. By the first century A.D., the Hindus were performing operations on irrational numbers.

Among the irrational numbers, one number aroused much curiosity and interest. This important number, denoted by π, and defined as the ratio of the circumference of a circle to its diameter, developed an entire history of its own. The number has an infinite decimal expansion, and occurs in a variety of mathematical ideas. It was calculated to several places by different civilizations, usually by a consideration of polygons with larger and larger number of sides. It was proved to be an irrational number by the middle of the eighteenth century. Modern computers have computed the decimal expansion of π to billions of places without finding an identifiable pattern. However, luckily for us, its truncated value—3.14—is quite sufficient for most calculations.

With the acceptance of the irrational numbers by the nineteenth century, there arose a need for a larger number system than the rational numbers that would incorporate the irrational numbers as well. This led to the creation of the set of real numbers that was defined to be the set of all numbers that have a decimal expansion. It consisted of the rational and irrational numbers, and came to be represented by a continuous line along which we can place each and every real number that we can think of. (While this is theoretically possible, in practice this turns out to be a little bit harder!) The conception of the real numbers as a set represented along a continuous line was an important idea that involved the work of two great nineteenth century German mathematicians, Weierstrass (1815 - 1897) and Dedekind (1831 - 1916); together, they laid the foundations of the modern field of mathematics known as real analysis.

Another important and dramatic area of mathematics that developed out of the interest in irrational numbers was the theory of infinity. The pioneer in this area was once again a German mathematician named Georg Cantor (1845 - 1918). Cantor, with his brilliant and totally original ideas, dared to go further into areas of real analysis than any of his predecessors. Using the simple idea of one-to-one correspondence, he came up with some revolutionary concepts. He proved the denseness of irrationals among the reals. Simply stated, the idea of denseness expresses the notion that there are an overwhelming number of irrational numbers among the real numbers. With such ideas as these, Cantor set out to tame infinity, a concept that bewildered mathematicians had even failed to accept existed until that time. As it was, Cantor faced much criticism from skeptical contemporaries. Nevertheless, today, Cantor is counted as one of the greatest of mathematicians, and the founder of the area of mathematics known as set theory. The twentieth century mathematician Hilbert praised Cantor's work in the highest of terms. As he put it, "No one will expel us from the paradise that Cantor has created."

One of the important results that Cantor proved stated that two line segments, regardless of their lengths, have the same number of points. Initially, this result was startling and difficult to comprehend. However, later, mathematicians used this result to resolve an ancient mathematical problem associated with Zeno (495 - 435 B.C.), who is said to have invented it. The problem was thus called Zeno's paradox, and can be stated as follows. Achilles and the tortoise run a race that ends when Achilles overtakes the tortoise. The tortoise is allowed a head start in the race and starts at a point ahead of Achilles. It is clear that at each instant of time, Achilles and the tortoise are at some point in their path, and each of them is at any given point no more than once. Now, both Achilles and the tortoise run for the same number of instants, and so they both go through the same number of points. However, to catch up with the tortoise, Achilles must run through more points (since he has a greater distance to cover) than does the tortoise. So, Achilles can never catch up with the tortoise. This apparent paradox that goes against our common sense confounded many philosophers and mathematicians. However, it can be resolved using Cantor's result stated earlier. The flaw lies in the reasoning that, to catch up with the tortoise, Achilles must run through more points than the tortoise. From Cantor's result, we know that two line segments, regardless of length, have the same number of points. Hence, as we would expect from intuition, Achilles can catch up with the tortoise and thus win the race.

Explanations Concerning Rationals and Irrationals

Section 7.1—Ratio and Proportion

A ratio is a pair of numbers, written as a : b, with b ≠ 0. Usually, numbers are written as a ratio as a means of comparison, for example if there are 3 girls and 5 boys in a room we say that the ratio of girls to boys is 3 : 5. It can also be used to express a fraction; for example we may write 7/10 as 7 : 10. Two ratios are said to be equal if they are represent equivalent fractions.

We say two ratios are in proportion if they represent equivalent fractions. Thus, if a : b = c : d, we say that a : b is in proportion to c : d. Thus, 3 : 4 is in proportion to 6 : 8, 5 : 7 is in proportion to 15 : 21.

Suppose two given ratios a : b and c : d are in proportion. We can graph the relationship between the two ratios by regarding a : b as the x and y coordinates of one point, and c : d as the x and y coordinates of another point. We can then plot these points on the Cartesian coordinate system. The graph obtained by joining these two points is the graph representing the proportion. Consider the ratios 3 : 4 and 9 : 12. They are in proportion. We can graph the relationship between the two ratios as follows.

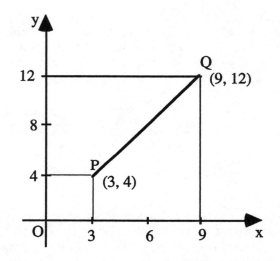

The line PQ represents the relationship between the two ratios.

Section 7.2—Decimals

A decimal representation is a means of writing a fraction in the base ten place value system. Numbers in this representation are written with a dot separating the whole numbers from the fractional part. The part after the dot successively represents tenths, hundredths, thousandths, and so on. Thus, 345.67 means 345 wholes and 67 hundredths, and 0.453 means no wholes and four hundred and fifty three thousandths. These two numbers could have also been written as 345 67/100 and 453/1000 respectively.

Section 7.3—Operations With Decimals
Addition or Subtraction of Two Decimal Numbers

We add two decimal numbers by simply writing the numbers to be added so that their decimal points lie in the same line. We now perform addition just as with integers, and in the answer we place the decimal point in line with the decimal point of the numbers to be added.

<u>Example 1</u>: Add 345.7256 + 16725.89.

<u>Solution</u>: To find this sum, we proceed as follows:

$$
\begin{array}{r}
345.7256 \\
+\ \underline{16725.8900} \\
17071.6156
\end{array}
$$

Note that any missing numbers after the two numbers have been lined up beyond the decimal point can be replaced by zeros. Similarly, 23.678 + 2.5 = 26.178.

Subtraction is performed in a similar fashion with decimal numbers.

<u>Example 2</u>: Subtract 235.98 from 300.

<u>Solution</u>:

$$
\begin{array}{r}
300.00 \\
-\ \underline{235.98} \\
64.02
\end{array}
$$

<u>Multiplication of Two Decimal Numbers</u>

To multiply two decimal numbers, we multiply the numbers as integers, then count off the total number of digits in both the numbers after the decimal point. We then place the decimal point in the product after counting off the same number of digits from the right.

<u>Example 3</u>:   Find 256.57 • 5.5.

<u>Solution</u>:

$$
\begin{array}{r}
256.57 \\
\text{x}\ \underline{\quad 5.5} \\
1411.135
\end{array}
$$

<u>Division Involving Two Decimal Numbers</u>

To divide one decimal number by another, we proceed as follows. First, convert the divisor to an integer by multiplying it with a suitable power of 10. Then, multiply the dividend by the same power of 10. Now, we perform division as with integers, placing the decimal point in the quotient directly above the decimal point in the dividend.

<u>Example 4</u>: Divide 35.256 by 2.53.

<u>Solution</u>: We first convert 2.53 to the integer 253 by multiplying it by 100.
Multiply 35.256 by 100. This gives 3525.6. we now divide 3525.6 by 253.

$$
\begin{array}{r}
\underline{\quad 13.935\quad} \\
253)3525.600 \\
\underline{253} \\
995 \\
\underline{759} \\
2366 \\
\underline{2277} \\
890 \\
\underline{759} \\
1310 \\
\underline{1265} \\
45
\end{array}
$$

As you can see, we may carry on this process indefinitely. We thus need to truncate it at some point. In this case, we have done so at the third decimal place. By convention, we check and make sure that the number following 5 in the quotient above is not greater than or equal to 5. If it is, then the quotient will be written as 13.936 instead of 13.935. This is called correction to the third decimal place.

Example 5: Perform the following operations. All answers that cannot be calculated exactly may be given correct up to three decimal places.

(a) 345.738 + 563.8
(b) 5627.65 – 4267.98
(c) 2.44 • 376.76
(d) 654.98 ÷ 6.76
(e) 87.37 + 67.345
(f) 2759 ÷ 4.21
(g) 2437.7 – 264.222
(h) 875.21 • 65.7

Solution: (a) 909.538 (b) 1359.67 (c) 919.2944 (d) 96.891 (e) 154.715 (f) 65.344 (g) 2173.478 (h) 57501.297

Section 7.4—Conversion from Decimal to Fractional Representation
The decimal form is another way to write a fraction, and we can write any given number in either of the two forms. We shall outline the procedures to do so here.

To convert a number from the decimal representation to the fractional representation, the whole numbers are written as the whole number part of a mixed fraction. To write the fractional part of the mixed fraction, we merely need to look at the number of places beyond the decimal point in any given number. If a number has only one number beyond the decimal point, then the number has only tenths, and we place the single digit over 10 to represent the fractional part of the number. Similarly, if the number has two digits beyond the decimal point, we place the two numbers over 100 to represent it as a fraction. This procedure may be continued to any number of digits beyond the decimal point.

Using the above process, we can write 2564.236 as 2564 236/1000, 67.89456 as 67 89456/100000, and –45.0031 as –45 31/10000.

Section 7.5—Conversion from Fractional to Decimal Representation
To convert a fractional expression into its decimal representation, we divide the numerator by the denominator of the fraction, adding zeros after the digits in the numerator have been exhausted. The decimal point is placed in the quotient before we operate with the first such zero in the dividend.

Example 6: Convert 23/4 to a decimal number.

Solution: We divide 23 by 4 as follows.

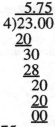

Thus, 3/4 = 5.75.

Example 7: Convert 1/3 to a decimal places.

Solution: If we perform the division as in the previous case, we find that we get 1/3 = 0.3333 ... The threes at the end of the number go on endlessly. We express this by placing a bar on top of the first three to indicate that from that point on, the 3 will repeat endlessly. Thus, we say, 1/3 = 0.3 (repeated).

Example 8: Convert 4/23 to a decimal place.

Solution: If we perform the division as before in this case, we will find that the process can go on for a long time. As with division, we thus truncate the process after two or three decimal points. In this case, this gives us 4/23 = 0.174.

Example 9: Convert the following numbers to the fraction form.
(a) 23.401 (b) 562.0001 (c) 0.89 (d) – 345.11011

Solution: (a) 23 401/1000 (b) 562 1/10000 (c) 89/100 (d) – 345 11011/100000

Example 10: Convert the following numbers to the decimal form. Give your answer correct to three decimal places.
(a) 3/8 (b) 45/7 (c) –4625/16 (d) 1/45

Solution: (a) 0.375 (b) 6.429 (c) –289.0625 (d) .02̄

Bibliography

Bennett, A B, & Nelson, L. T. (1994). A conceptual model for solving percent problems. *Mathematics Teaching in the Middle School, 1*, 20-25.

Bezuk, N. S. & Armstrong, B. E. (1992). "Activities: Understanding fraction multiplication.*Mathematics Teacher, 85*, 729-733, 739-744.

Bezuk, N. S. & Armstrong, B. E. (1993). Activities: Understanding division of fractions. *Mathematics Teacher, 86*, 43-46, 56-60.

Boling, B. A. (1985). A different method for solving percentage problems. Mathematics *Teacher, 78*, 523-524.

Coburn, T. G. (1986). Percentage and the hand calculator. *Mathematics Teacher, 79*, 361-367.

Cramer, K. & Bezuk. N. (1991). Multiplication of fractions: Teaching for understanding. *Arithmetic Teacher, 39*(3), 34-37.6

Cramer, K. A., Post, T. R. & Behr, M. J. (1989). Interpreting proportional relationships. *Mathematics Teacher 82*, 445-452.

Cramer, K., & Karnowski, L (1995) The importance of informal language in representing mathematical ideas. *Teaching Children Mathematics, 1*, 332-335.

Cramer, K., & Post,T. R. (1993). Making connections: A case for proportionality. *Arithmetic Teacher 40*, 342-346.

Cramer, K., Post, T. R., & Currier, S. (1993). Learning and teaching ratio and proportion: Research implications. In D. T. Owens (Ed.), *Research ideas for the classroom: Middle grades mathematics* (pp. 159-178). Old Tappan, NJ: Macmillan.

Dewar, J. M. (1984). Another look at the teaching of percent. *Arithmetic Teacher, 31*, 48-49.

Edwards, F. M. (1987). Geometric figures make the LCM obvious. *Arithmetic Teacher, 34* , 17-18.

Erickson, D. K. (1990). "Activities: Percentages and Cuisenaire rods. *Mathematics Teacher, 83*, 648-654.

Glatzer, D. J. (1984). Teaching percentage: Ideas and suggestions. *Arithmetic Teacher, 31*, 24-26.

Grossman, A. S. (1983). Decimal notation: An important research finding. *ArithmeticTeacher* , *30*, 32-33.

Haubner, M. A. (1992). Percents: Developing meaning through models. *Arithmetic Teacher, 40*, 232-234.

Hiebert, J. (1987). Research report: Decimal fractions. *Arithmetic Teacher, 34*, 22-23.

Huinker, D. (1992). Decimals and calculators make sense. In J. T. Fey (Ed.), *Calculators in mathematics education* (pp 56-04). Reston, VA: National Council of Teachers of Mathematics.

Hurd, S. P. (1991). Egyptian fractions: Ahmes to Fibonacci to today." *Mathematics Teacher, 84*, 561-568.

Langford, K., & Sarullo, A. (1993). Introductory common and decimal fraction concepts. In R. J. Jensen (Ed.), *Research ideas for the classroom: Early childhood mathematics* (pp. 223-247). OId Tappan. NJ: Macmillan.

Meeks, K. I. (1992). Decimals, rounding, and apportionment. Mathematics *Teacher, 85*, 523-525.

Nowlin, D. (1996). Division with fractions. *Mathematics Teaching in the Middle School*, 2, 116- 119.

Ott, J. M. (1990). A unified approach to multiplying fractions. *Arithmetic Teacher, 37*(7), 47-49.

Owens, D. T. & Super, D. B.(1993). Teaching and reaming decimal fractions. In D T. Owens (Ed.), Research *ideas for* the *classroom:* Middle grades *mathematics (pp.* 137-158). Old Tappan, NJ: Macmillan.

Payne, J. N., &Towsley, A.E. (1990). Implementing the *Standards*: Implications of NCTM's *Standards* for teaching fractions and decimals. *Arithmetic Teacher, 37,* 23-26.

Payne, J. N., Towsley, A. E., & Huinker. D. M. (1990). Fractions and decimals. In J. N. Payne (Ed), *Mathematics for the young child (pp.* 175-200). Reston, VA: National Council of Teachers of Mathematics.

Prevost, F. J. (1984). Teaching rational numbers: Junior high school. *Arithmetic Teacher, 31*(6), 43-46.

Quintero, A. H. (1987). Helping children understand ratios. *Arithmetic Teacher, 34,* 17-21.

Rees, J. M. (1987). Two-sided pies: Help for improper fractions and mixed numbers. *Arithmetic Teacher, 35,* 28-32.

Sarver, V. T., Jr. (1986). Why does a negative times a negative produce a positive? *Mathematics Teacher, 79,* 178-180.

Steiner, E. E. (1987). Division of fractions: Developing conceptual sense with dollars and cents. *Arithmetic Teacher, 34,* 36-42.

Thompson, C. S., & Walker, V. (1996). Connecting decimals and other mathematical content *Teaching Children Mathematics, 2,* 496-502.

Vance, J.M. (1986). Ordering decimals and fractions: A diagnostic study. *Focus on Laming Problems in Mathematics, 8*(2), 51-59.

Vance, J. M. (1986). Estimating decimal products: An instructional sequence. In H. L. Schoen (Ed.), *Estimation and mental computation* (pp. 127-134!. Reston, VA: National Council of Teachers of Mathematics.

Wiebe, J. H. (1986). Manipulating percentages. Arithmetic Teacher, 33(5), 23-26.

Williams, S. E. & Copley, J. V. (1994). Promoting classroom dialogue: Using calculators to discover patterns in dividing decimals. *Mathematics Teaching in the Middle School, 1,* 72-75.

Williams, S. E., & Copley, J. V. (1994). Promoting classroom dialogue: Using calculators to discover patterns in dividing decimals. *Mathematics Teaching in the Middle School, 1,* 72-75.

Zawojewski, J. (1983). Initial decimal concepts: Are they really so easy? *Arithmetic Teacher, 30*(7). 52-56.

Chapter 8: Patterns & Functions

Chapter Overview:

The concept of function is a central theme, a big idea, running through many areas of mathematics. In this chapter you can learn about a historical, social, and cultural context for functions, and examine some concepts and procedures involving function ideas.

Big Mathematical Ideas:

> problem-solving strategies, functions & relations, representation, conjecturing, verifying, mathematical structure

NCTM Standards Links:

> *K - 4:* Mathematics as problem solving; Mathematics as communication; Mathematics as reasoning; Mathematical connections; Patterns & relationships
>
> *5 - 8:* Mathematics as problem solving; Mathematics as communication; Mathematics as reasoning; Mathematical connections; Patterns & functions

Chapter Outline:

Historical/Social/Cultural Notes about Patterns & Functions

The distance that a car travels depends on the speed of the car, and the amount of time spent traveling. The profit obtained from the sale of furniture depends on the cost of the raw materials and labor, and the number of pieces of furniture sold. The more time you spend practicing tennis, the better you are likely to get at it. The more water you pour into a vessel, the higher the level of the water in it. All the preceding statements reveal a relationship between two quantities. Moreover, the relationship between the two quantities can be expressed in a certain way. In mathematics, such relationships are called functions, or functional relationships. They express the relationship between two (or more) related quantities called variables. The study of functions has become one of the important branches of mathematics today.

It is difficult to trace the history of the study of functions; in fact, the task may be quite impossible keeping in mind that almost since the beginning of time, human beings were curious about nature and were always attempting to establish connections between two phenomena that appeared to be related. The Greek philosophers were intensely involved in looking for such relationships. Their primary aim was to establish causal relationships, that is, they were looking for relationships that explained why certain things happened in nature. The trouble with the relationships that were established at the time was that most of them were erroneous. Being obsessed with why things happen, the philosophers were often misled by the apparent aim of a phenomenon as related to human beings. For example, they would explain that rain took place because it was essential for crops to grow.

An important change took place in the study of mathematics around the year 1600 A.D. The thinking that led to this change began with the work of the Italian mathematician and scientist Galileo. Galileo realized that instead of looking for explanations of an event, it may be useful to quantify the relationships involved in an event. In other words, he was looking for formulas that would represent the exact relationships between different variables. Much of the early work on such functions was related to one phenomenon — the movement of a physical object. Thus began the study of concepts related to motion such as distance, velocity, acceleration, momentum, and inertia. Later, scientists added other concepts such as temperature, volume, pressure, and power.

The study of functions has now progressed much beyond the time of Galileo. In particular, in the seventeenth century, the study of moving bodies led to an entirely new field of mathematics related to functions. This was the invention of calculus by two great mathematicians, Newton and Leibnitz, working independently on opposite sides of the English channel—Newton in England, Leibnitz in Germany. Even in the Age of Genius, as the seventeenth century is often referred to, the invention of calculus was a landmark that was one of the most important in human history and it succeeded in revolutionizing the study of mathematics. Concepts in calculus are beyond the scope of this chapter, so we will merely state that this area of mathematics involves looking at physical quantities by studying what happens at the microscopic level—the smallest intervals of time, the infinitesimal bits of length, and the tiniest changes in temperature.

While functions are useful in studying and modeling numerous relationships between variables that occur in nature and in everyday life, in the twentieth century mathematicians and scientists have found that there are phenomena, such as the prices in the stock market, where it is impossible to find precise mathematical relationships to represent these phenomena. This realization started a new theory, appropriately titled chaos theory and a new form of geometry called fractal geometry. The term fractal (from the Latin "fractus" meaning broken) was coined by Benoit Mandlebrot, a professor at Yale University. In 1982, he wrote a book titled, "The Fractal Geometry of Nature." This was the first major work on the subject, and the sets that he studied were called Mandlebrot Sets.

We will describe two fractal patterns here. The construction begins with a segment that we separate into thirds. In the next step, we construct an equilateral triangle "bump" in the middle third of the segment. In the next step, we construct equilateral triangle bumps on the middle third of each side of the big triangle. We now continue to repeat this pattern infinitely many times. The curve that results from this process is known as a Koch curve.

1st step

2nd step

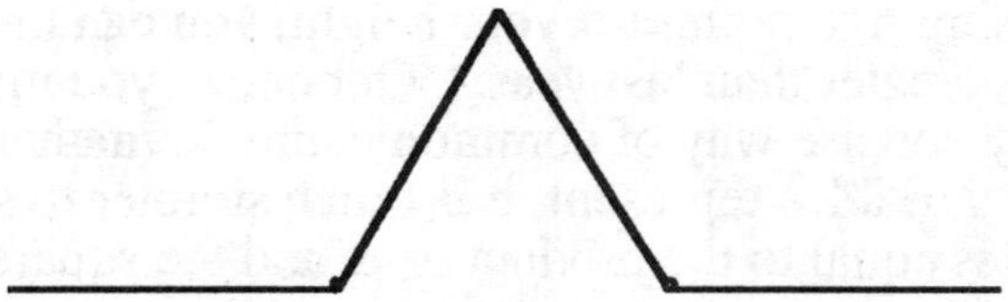

3rd step

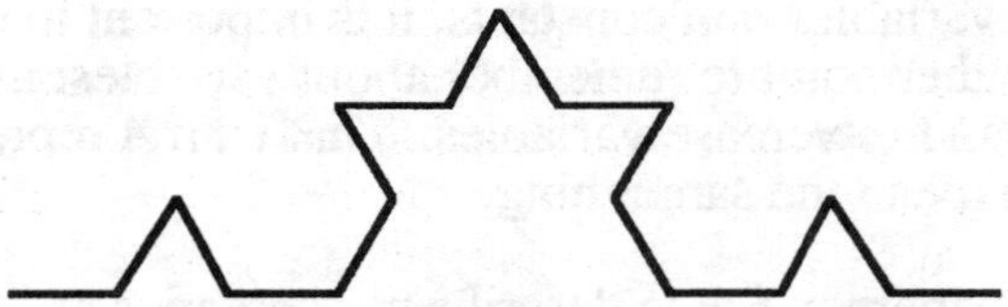

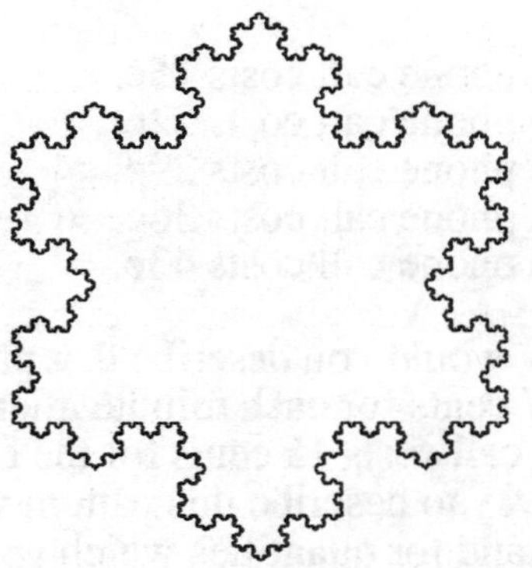

Koch curve snowflake

There are two important aspects to this curve. Firstly, each new triangle that is constructed is similar to the original triangle. Thus, we say the Koch curve is self similar. It will look exactly the same no matter how many times it is magnified. Secondly, the curve has a finite area—the entire picture can be placed inside a circle. The area of the entire diagram cannot be more than the area of the circle. However, the Koch curve has an infinite perimeter! We thus have an amazing geometric figure here—physically, you may think of it as being a fixed amount of land that needs an infinite amount of wire fencing to cover its boundaries!

Another such curve that is easy to construct is a Sierpienski Gasket. Here, we start with a black triangle (not necessarily equilateral, but we may start with one for convenience). Now, we successively remove similar smaller triangles from the larger one, making them white to distinguish them from the first one. Thus, we obtain what is called a Sierpienski Gasket.

Explanations Concerning Patterns & Functions

Section 8.1—Variables

The root word of *variable* is *vary*, which means *change*. A variable is simply a *quantity* or a quality that can change, or has the potential to change. A person's height is an example of a *quantitative variable* and the color of the sky is an example of a *qualitative variable*.

It is customary in mathematics, as well as in other sciences, to use symbols (typically, letters) to represent variables. For example, you may use the letter h to represent your height. Once you tell someone that you are using h to represent your height, you can then say things like, "h is 65 inches," or, "This year, h is greater than last year." Of course, you may not talk like this in everyday life, but it is a very concise way of communicating in mathematics. For example once you've indicated what your variables represent, it is much simpler to say or write $A = \pi r^2$ than it is to say, "The area of a circle is equal to the product of pi and the square of the circle's radius."

Note, by the way, that in πr^2, π is not a variable. Here, π represents a *constant*. Because we use letters to represent both variables *and* constants, it is important to distinguish between the two if you are using both. One other point to remember about variables: in mathematics, we distinguish between upper- and lowercase variables. That is, if A represents the area of a circle, then a should not be used to mean the same thing.

Using variables to describe patterns: Some describe mathematics as "the science of patterns." In mathematics, we are always searching for patterns, as well as for ways to describe them.

Consider the following:
- A 1-minute long-distance phone call costs 15¢.
- A 2-minute long-distance phone call costs 22¢.
- A 3-minute long-distance phone call costs 29¢.
- A 4-minute long-distance phone call costs 36¢.
- A 5-minute long-distance phone call costs 43¢.

Do you notice a pattern? How would you describe that pattern? Some might notice that the cost of a phone call increases by 7 cents for each minute after the first. So, we might describe this pattern as "A long-distance phone call costs 15 cents for the first minute, and 7 cents for each additional minute." But another way to describe this pattern would be with *variables*—letters of the alphabet which are meant to stand for quantities which *vary* (in this case, the length of the phone call and the cost of the phone call).

So, we would like to try to describe this pattern with a variable. At this point, you may or may not see a pattern. If you have trouble seeing a pattern, it is sometimes helpful to *try a special case*. By working on a special case, it is sometimes a little easier to start noticing patterns. Then, once you've worked on a special case, try to *generalize* the pattern using variables. Notice the similarities in the next two examples. The first is a *special case* (we randomly decided to find the cost of a 47-minute phone call). The second looks just like the first, except that it uses a variable n to represent the length in minutes of the phone call.

Example 1: How much would a 47-minute phone call cost?

Solution: Well, from the pattern above, it would cost 15 cents for the first minute, and 7 cents for each of the remaining 46 minutes. So, a 47-minute phone call will cost 15 cents plus 46 times 7 cents. We could write this as:

$$15¢ + 46 \cdot 7¢$$

<u>Example 2</u>: How much would an *n*-minute phone call cost?

<u>Solution</u>: Well, from the pattern above, it would cost 15 cents for the first minute, and 7 cents for each of the remaining *n*-1 minutes. So, an *n*-minute phone call will cost 15 cents plus *n*-1 times 7 cents.

We could simplify this last sentence even more by using a little more mathematical notation:

- An *n*-minute phone call costs $[15 + 7(n-1)]$¢.

Now that we have this generalization, it is easy to find the cost of *any* phone call. What would a 2-hour phone call cost?

- A 120-minute phone call costs $[15 + 7(120-1)]$ ¢.

<u>Example 3</u>: What is the nth term in the sequence 2, 5, 10, 17, 26, . . . ?

<u>Solution</u>: There is no surefire way of finding patterns, but sometimes it helps to list terms individually as follows:

- The 1st term is 2
- The 2nd term is 5
- The 3rd term is 10
- The 4th term is 17
- The 5th term is 26

Then, see if you can find a relationship between the number of the term, and the value of that term. This is often a *guess and check* process. For example, you may notice in *"The 3rd term is 10"* that you can start with the 3 in "3rd," multiply it by 3 and add 1 to get 10. So, maybe the rule is:

- The *n*th term is *n* times 3 plus 1.

But, you will quickly realize that this description does not fit any of the other terms in the list. After you try a few other things, you may notice that:

- The 3rd term is 3 times 3 plus 1.
- The 4th term is 4 times 4 plus 1.
- The 5th term is 5 times 5 plus 1.

The pattern here seems to be:

- The nth term is n times n plus 1.

Or:

- The nth term is $n^2 + 1$.

Does this pattern work for the first two terms as well? Indeed it does. So, we have found a pattern and described it with a variable. (Note, however, that there may be *another* pattern that is very different from the one we found. Mathematicians will quickly remind us that, no matter how many terms of a sequence you start with, there could be *many* different patterns that would adequately describe the sequence.)

Section 8.2—Dependent and Independent Variables

Sometimes, when dealing with two variables, it may be that one of the variables depends on the other. For example, we might say that the length of a shadow, *s*, *depends* on the time of day, *t*. In this situation, we would call *s* a *dependent variable*, because it depends on the variable *t*. *t*, on the other hand, would be called an *independent variable*. In fact, in most situations involving time, time is generally considered the independent variable. In some situations involving two or more variables, it may be that neither variable is dependent or independent. For example, in the equation $x + y = 10$, where we don't really know what either variable represents, there would be no reason to conclude that either variable is dependent or independent.

<u>Graphing independent and dependent variables</u>: It is customary, when graphing the relationship between a dependent and an independent variable, to place the *independent variable on the horizontal axis*, and the *dependent variable on the vertical axis*. So, if we were to graph the relationship between time of day and length of shadow, as described above, the axes would look like this:

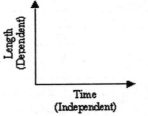

It is not *wrong* to place the dependent variable on the horizontal axis, but it is generally understood that the independent variable is always associated with that axis.

<u>Function notation with independent and dependent variables</u>: Suppose, in the scenario described above, that at 7 a.m. the length of a shadow is 3 feet. One way to show this relationship would be in a table:

Time, *t* (hours)	Shadow Length, *s* (feet)
7	3

Another way would be to plot the point on a graph:

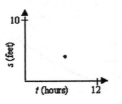

A third way would be to use *function notation* (for more details, see the section on function notation). We might say that:

$$s(7) = 3$$

Here, *s* is not only the name of a variable, it is also the name of the *function*. *s*(*t*) would represent the shadow length *s* at time *t*. Notice that the value of the shadow *function* depends on the time. In function notation, the *function* (in this case, *s*) is the dependent variable. The value that we enter in parentheses is the independent variable.

Section 8.3—Functions

How are month and average daily temperature related? You might say something like, "The summer months are warmer than the winter months," or, "The average daily temperature in May is about the same in September." How could you be more precise in describing such a relationship? One way is with a *function*. In mathematics, a function allows us to describe a relationship between two or more variables (in this case, the variables would be month and temperature).

Functions can take on many forms. Four of the most common are: tables, graphs, ordered pairs, and function notation.

Here is the month/temperature function in *table* form:

Month	Average Daily Temperature (°F)
January	23
February	19
March	31
April	44
May	52
June	65
July	72
August	68
September	54
October	41
November	39
December	28

As a side note, since temperature *depends* on the month, "temperature" is the *dependent* "variable," and month is the independent variable. See Section 8.2.

This same function could be represented as a *graph*:

Average Daily Temperature By Month

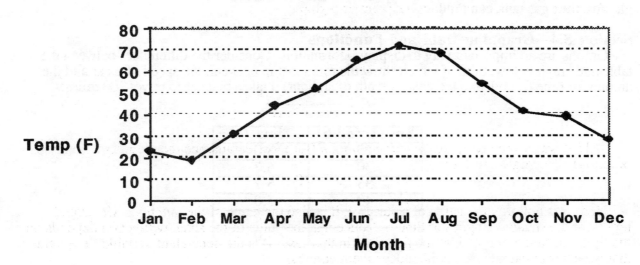

Notice that the independent variable is plotted along the horizontal axis, and the dependent along the vertical axis. Also notice that the points between the months were connected. This is not a requirement, but is sometimes done to help make trends clearer.

A third way to represent a function of two variables is with a list of *ordered pairs*. (Jan, 23) is an example of an ordered pair. It's called "ordered" pair because the order of the two variables is important. Typically, the independent variable is listed first in an ordered pair. There are, of course, eleven other ordered pairs we could list from the data in the table or graph.

A fourth way to represent a function is with *function notation*: symbols which help clarify the relationship between the variables. Since, in this function, the temperature depends on the month, we could say that temperature *is a function of* the month. Using the variables t and m to represent time and month, respectively, we can say, "t is a function of m." Function notation allows us to concisely write out relationships. For example, rather than saying, "The average daily temperature in May is 52° F," we could simply write:

$$t(\text{May}) = 52$$

Similarly, "$t(\text{December}) = 28$" would be another way of saying, "December's average daily temperature is 28° F."

Function notation also allows us to describe patterns we find in numerical relationships. For example, suppose you know that your car can travel 30 miles on a gallon of gasoline. Using g and d to represent gallons of gas and the distance your car can travel, respectively, then, using function notation, we may write:

$$d(g) = 30 \cdot g$$

This equation is read, "d of g equals 30 times g."

In a function, the domain is the set of values that can be used for the independent variable. In this example, the domain would be from 0 to whatever is the capacity of your car's gas tank. The range, or the set of values that can be taken on by the dependent variable, would be from 0 miles (corresponding to the miles a car can travel on 0 gallons of gasoline) to 30 times the number of gallons your gas tank can hold.

Section 8.4—Graphing Data and Functions

Graphs are an important way to display information. Consider the differences between the table and graph below, both of which show the relationship between the speed of a car and the amount of time (rounded to the nearest tenth of an hour) it takes that car to travel 200 miles:

Speed (mi/h)	Time (h)
25	8.0
30	6.7
35	5.7
40	5.0
45	4.4
50	4.0

Time it takes to drive 200 miles

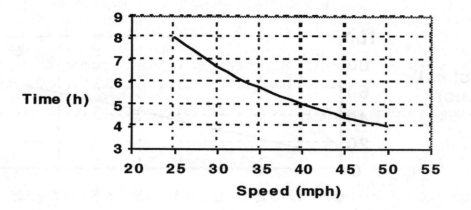

A limitation of the table is that it only shows six pairs of numbers. If you wanted to know how long the trip would take if you were traveling at 33 miles per hour, you could use the table to make only a rough estimate: somewhere between 5.7 and 6.7 hours. However, by looking at the graph, it is easier to get a better estimate. Starting at about 33 on the horizontal axis, and moving vertically until you meet the graph, reveals that the time it takes would be very close to 6 hours. (Actually, the amount of time it would take would be 200 ÷ 33 ≈ 6.1 miles per hour.)

<u>Graphs should convey meaning</u>: Look at the graph below. What does it tell you?

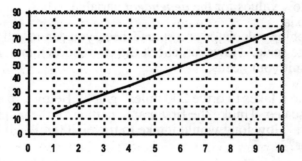

Without more information, this graph is meaningless. What if it had a title that said, "The cost of a long-distance phone call?" This may help a little, but it still does not make clear what all the numbers mean. Suppose the vertical axis said "Cost." That still would not be specific enough, because it is not clear whether cost is being measured in cents or dollars. To make a graph meaningful, you should include a title that states clearly what the graph is about, and axis labels that indicate the units of measurement. Below is that same graph, but with a title and labels. Does it make more sense now?

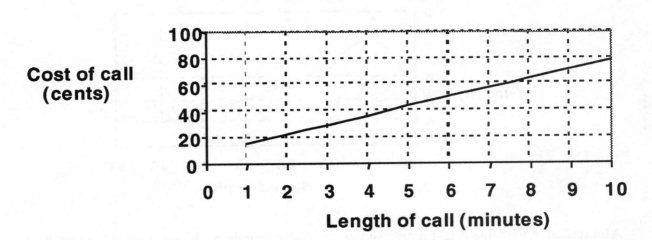

Cost of a long-distance phone call

Choose your scale carefully: When creating a graph, it is important to choose meaningful scales. Scales should also be uniform. That is, the difference between adjacent tick marks on the same axis should be the same all the way along that axis. Before making a graph, you should look carefully at the data you plan to graph.

- Look at the high and low values for the *independent* variable. These should help you determine a scale for the *horizontal* axis.
- Look at the high and low values for the *dependent* variable. These should help you determine a scale for the *vertical* axis.
- If you are using a graphing calculator or a spreadsheet, you can usually let the technology "guess" the appropriate scale. However, check the instruction manual for instructions on how to adjust the scale to suit your needs.

Look back at the "Time it takes to drive 200 miles" graph. Below are examples of that same graph with inappropriate scales. Unlike the first graph, neither of the graphs below can help you answer a question such as, "How long would it take to travel 200 miles if I were traveling at a speed of 43 miles per hour?"

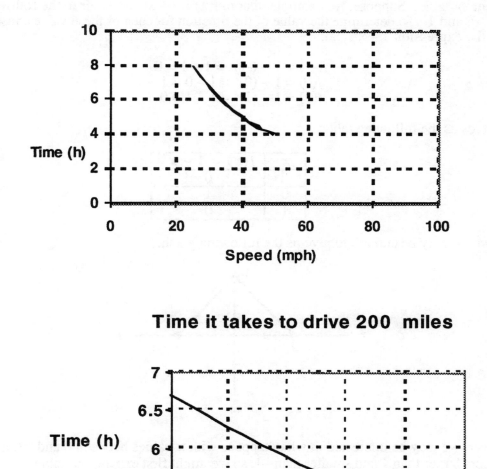

Time it takes to drive 200 miles

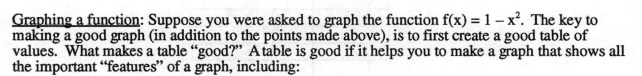

<u>Graphing a function</u>: Suppose you were asked to graph the function $f(x) = 1 - x^2$. The key to making a good graph (in addition to the points made above), is to first create a good table of values. What makes a table "good?" A table is good if it helps you to make a graph that shows all the important "features" of a graph, including:

- Where the graph crosses the horizontal and vertical axes
- Where the graph "changes directions" (e.g., where does it switch from going "up" to going "down?")
- High points and low points on the graph
- "Long range" behavior (e.g., does the graph "keep going higher" the farther you go to the right? Does it "keep getting closer to a certain value?")

Sometimes, it takes a little trial and error to get a good graph. It is a good idea, though, to at least input some negative values (when appropriate), some positive values, and zero for the independent variable. Suppose, for example, that in $f(x) = 1 - x^2$, we enter in the following x-values: -1, 0, and 1. To determine the value of the function for each of these values, insert each of them into the expression $1 - x^2$. So,

$$f(-1) = 1 - (-1)^2 = 1 - 1 = 0$$
$$f(0) = 1 - (0)^2 = 1 - 0 = 1$$
$$f(1) = 1 - (1)^2 = 1 - 1 = 0$$

This gives us the following table:

x	$f(x) = 1 - x^2$
-1	0
0	1
1	0

This would only be enough to give us the following graph:

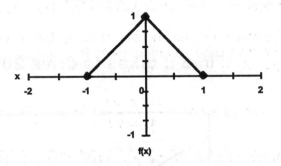

However, we may be interested in what happens with x-values between 0 and ±1, as well as with numbers larger than 1 and smaller than −1, so we might first expand our table:

x	$f(x) = 1 - x^2$
-1.5	-1.25
-1	0
-0.75	0.4375
-0.5	0.75
-0.25	0.9375
0	1
0.25	0.9375
0.5	0.75
0.75	0.4375
1	0
1.5	-1.25

Notice how much more is revealed by graphing these numbers:

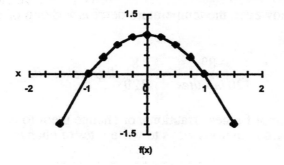

In the first graph, we were not only unable to see the curved nature of the graph, but we also don't know what happened to the graph outside of the range of x = -1 to x = 1. In this graph, we are able to get a much better understanding of how the function "behaves."

Section 8.5—Slope and Rate of Change

Suppose that, on a four-hour trip, you traveled 212 miles. How fast did you travel?

It is likely that, during the entire trip, you traveled at many different speeds. Your average speed, however, can easily be calculated. Average speed is simply the total distance traveled, divided by the total time traveled. In this case, then,

$$Average\ Speed = \frac{212\ miles}{4\ hours} = 53\ miles/hour$$

Average speed is an example of a rate of change. A rate of change compares, using division, how much one variable changes to how much another variable changes. Average speed, for example, compares change in distance to change in time.

Let's look at another example. Below is a list of times and temperatures for a two-hour period, taken every 15 minutes:

Time	Temperature (°F)
2:00	60
2:15	63
2:30	61
2:45	59
3:00	56
3:15	57
3:30	57
3:45	55
4:00	52

During time intervals where the temperature increased, we say that there has been a positive rate of change. During a decrease in temperature, the rate of change is negative. For example, from 2:00 until 2:15, the rate of change was:

$$\frac{3°}{15\ minutes} = \frac{3}{15}\ degrees/minute$$

From 2:00 until 4:00, however, the temperature decreased 8 degrees. So, the rate of change was:

$$\frac{-8°}{120\ minutes} = -\frac{8}{120}\ degrees/minute$$

Of course, you could simplify these fractions, or change them to decimals, or work in hours instead of minutes. There are numerous ways to write rates of change, so long as you remember to:

- *divide* the change in one variable by the change in another
- use the appropriate *units* (e.g., if you divided dollars by pounds, the rate of change will be in "dollars per pound.")

Let's take a look at the same time/temperature data in graph form:

Can you tell, by looking at the graph, during which time periods the temperature was increasing, decreasing, and not changing? You may have noticed that the "steepness" of the line, as well as its direction (whether it slants up or down as you move left to right) is a good indicator of how and how fast the temperature is changing. The when the temperature is increasing, and the graph is moving upward from left to right, we say that the graph has a positive slope during that time. Similarly, during a decrease, when the graph is moving downward from left to right, we say that the graph has a negative slope. It makes sense then, that from 3:15 to 3:30, when the change in temperature was 0°, the graph has a slope of zero.

By now, you might also have noticed that when rate of change is positive, so is the slope. When rate of change is negative, so is the slope. And, when rate of change is zero, so is the slope. This is not a coincidence. Slope and rate of change mean the same thing, and are calculated the same way. As we calculated above, the rate of change from 2:00 to 2:15 is:

$$\frac{3°}{15\ minutes} = \frac{3}{15}\ degrees/minute$$

Similarly, we can say that the slope of the line segment from (2:00, 60°) to (2:15, 63°) is 3/15. Note that two points on a graph need not be connected in order to calculate the slope between them. For example, we calculated above that the rate of change from 2:00 to 4:00 was:

$$\frac{-8°}{120\ minutes} = -\frac{8}{120}\ degrees/minute$$

Similarly, we can say that the slope of the line segment (if we were to draw it) from (2:00, 60°) to (4:00, 52°) is –8/120.

Section 8.6—Finding the Best/Minimum/Maximum Solution

Chances are, if you drive to school, there are many different routes you could take. Which of these routes is best? Chances are, you try to take the route that takes a minimum amount of time. But how do you know that your route is best?

Quite often, we are faced with situations where we are looking for a best (or minimum or maximum) solution. Whether it's choosing a route to school, deciding which car to buy, or planning a vacation, we regularly have numerous options from which we need to choose only one. In business, the need to find a best solution arises all the time. For example, suppose you are in a birdhouse building business. It costs you five dollars to make a birdhouse. You need to decide how much to charge people who want to buy your birdhouses. If you charge $5.01, you may sell a lot of birdhouses, but you may not make very much money. If you charge $100, you will earn a lot of money from the sale of the birdhouse, but may not find anyone willing to spend that much money. A good selling price would likely be between $5 and $100. But where? The answer depends on a lot of factors, and you may never find the answer without first trying a few good guesses.

Let's look at another situation. You have 26 feet of fencing available, and wish to build a small rectangular pen for your pet Chihuahua. Of course, as you probably know, Chihuahuas love to run around, so you would like to make the pen as large as possible. You'd like to give Chip (that is your Chihuahua's name, right?) the largest possible area using all 26 feet of fence. How do you go about finding the maximum area?

While some advanced mathematical topics, such as differential calculus, could be used to find the solution, a simple system of guessing and checking will often do the trick.

Ok, what if you made a rectangle that measures 3 feet on one side, and 10 feet on the other? Well, you could certainly try that rectangle as your first guess, but it may be more helpful to first plan out your guesses. You might look for a way to organize your guesses so that you don't try any of the same guesses twice, and you don't skip over any important guesses.

So, maybe we could start with a guess of a 1 foot by 12 feet rectangle, then try 2 feet by 11 feet, and then 3 feet by 10 feet, and so on. Notice, by the way, that we skipped over a lot of guesses here. We haven't listed 1.25 feet by 11.75 feet, or 2.718 feet by 10.282 feet. Maybe one of these is the right answer. It could be. But, since there's no way we could ever try all possibilities, we will start with some that are easy to work with, and see what happens.

Length (feet)	Width (feet)	Perimeter (feet)	Area (square feet)
1	12	26	12
2	11	26	22
3	10	26	30
4	9	26	36
5	8	26	40
6	7	26	42
7	6	26	42
8	5	26	40

Notice that we stopped short of a complete list. Do you see why? If you look carefully, you should notice that the 5 feet by 8 feet rectangle is really the same as the 8 feet by 5 feet rectangle. The second half of the list would look just like the first half. It seems, from looking at our list, that the maximum area seems to be when the rectangle measures 6 feet by 7 feet (or 7 by 6). So, have we found the best solution? Maybe. Maybe not. It's not always easy to tell. However, if you look at the "Area" column, you may notice that the numbers increase until they sort of "peak" when the length and width are almost the same. Is it possible that the area actually peaks somewhere between the 6 by 7 and 7 by 6 entries? One way to find out is to "zoom in" on those two entries, focusing our attention on some of the entries *between* them:

Length (feet)	Width (feet)	Perimeter (feet)	Area (square feet)
6	7	26	42
6.25	6.75	26	42.1875
6.5	6.5	26	42.25
6.75	6.25	26	42.1875
7	6	26	42

So, we have improved on our 6 by 7 solution. With a square pen measuring 6.5 feet on each side, Chip could have 42.25 square feet of running area. Is there a better solution? Just because an answer "feels right" does not always mean that it is right. In this situation, however, it turns out that the square pen really does produce the maximum area.

Remember, when looking for a best solution, be systematic. Be on the lookout for patterns that can simplify your work. And be forewarned: just because someone asks for a "best" solution doesn't always mean that there is a best solution. For example, if you were asked to find the maximum perimeter possible for a rectangle whose area is 10 square meters, your search would never end. There is no maximum!

Bibliography

Ajose, S. (1991). Activities: Patterns in the hundred chart- Part 1 - Part 2. *Mathematics Teacher, 84*, 43-48, 118-124.

Bidwell, J. K. (1987). Using reflections to find symmetric and asymmetric patterns. *Arithmetic Teacher, 34*(7), 10-15.

Coburn, T. G. (1993). Patterns: *Addenda series, grades K-4*. Reston, VA: National Council of Teachers of Mathematics.

Coxford, A. F. (Ed.). (1988). *The ideas of algebra.* Reston, VA: National Council of Teachers of Mathematics.

Day, R. P. (1995). Using functions to make mathematical connections. In P. A. House (Ed.), *Connecting mathematics across the curriculum* (pp. 54-64). Reston, VA: National Council of Teachers of Mathematics.

Edwards, E. L. (Ed.). (1990). *Algebra for everyone.* Reston, VA: National Council of Teachers of Mathematics.

Emie, K. T. (1995). Mathematics and quilting. In P. A. House (Ed), *Connecting mathematics across the curriculum (pp.* 17~176) Reston, VA: National Council of Teachers of Mathematics.

Fey, J. T., & Heid, M. K. (1995). *Concepts in algebra: A technological approach.* Dedham, MA: Janson.

Geer, C. P. (1992). Exploring patterns, relations, and functions. *Arithmetic Teacher, 39*(9), 19-21.

Giambrone, T. M. (1983). Challenges for enriching the curriculum: Algebra. *Mathematics Teacher, 76*, 262-263.

Hastings, E. H., & Yates, D. S. (1983). Microcomputer unit: Graphing straight lines. *Mathematics Teacher , 76*, I81-186.

Kieran. C. (1991). Research into practice: Helping to make the transition to algebra. *Arithmetic Teacher, 38, 49-51.*

Litwiller, B. H., & Duncan, D. R. (1985). Pentagonal patterns in the addition table. *Arithmetic Teacher, 32*, 36-38.

Loewen, A. C. (1991). Lima beans, paper cups, and algebra. *Arithmetic Teacher, 38*, 34-37.

Morelli, L. (1992). A visual approach to algebra concepts. *Mathematics Teacher, 85*, 434-437.

Nibbelink, W. H. (1990). Teaching equations. *Arithmetic Teacher, 38, 48-51.*

Onslow, B. (1990). Pentominoes revisited. *Arithmetic Teacher, 37*, 5-9.

Osbome, A., & Wilson, P. S. (1988). Moving to algebraic thought. In T. R. Post (Ed.), *Teaching mathematics in grades K-8: Research-based methods (pp.* 421—442). Needham Heights, MA: Allyn & Bacon.

Peitgen, H., Jürgens, H., & Saupe, D. (1992). *Fractals for the classroom part one: Introduction to fractals and chaos.* New York:Springer-Verlag.

Peitgen, H., Jürgens, H., Saupe, D., Maletsky, E., Perciante, T., & Yunker, L. (1991*). Fractals for the classroom: Strategic activities volume one.* New York: Springer-Verlag.

Phillips, E. (1991). *Patterns and functions: Addenda series, grades 5 - 8.* Reston, VA: National Council of Teachers of Mathematics.

Schoenfeld, A. H., & Arcavi, A. (1988). On the meaning of variable. *Mathematics Teacher, 81*, 424-427.

Schultz, J. E. (1991). Implementing the *Standards*: Teaching informal algebra. *Arithmetic Teacher, 38*, 34-37.

Thompson, A. G. (1985). On patterns, conjectures, and proof: Developing students' mathematical thinking. *Arithmetic Teacher, 33*(1), 20-23.

Van de Walle, J. A. & Holbrook, H. (1987). Patterns, thinking, and problem solving. *Arithmetic Teacher, 31*(8), 9-12.

Wagner, S. (1983). What are these things called variables? *Mathematics Teacher, 76,* 474-479.

Wagner, S., & Parker, S. (1993). Advancing algebra. In S. Wagner (Ed.), *Research* ideas *for the classroom: High school mathematics* (pp. 119-139). Old Tappan, NJ: Macmillan.

Wilson, M. R., & Shealy, B. E. (1995). Experiencing function relationships with a viewing tube. In P. A. House (Ed.), *Connecting mathematics across the curriculum* (pp. 219-224) Reston, VA: National Council of Teachers of Mathematics.

Chapter 9: Geometry

Chapter Overview:

Geometry is among the richest and oldest branches of mathematics. We think of geometry as the study of space experiences. This study focuses mainly on shapes as abstractions from the environment, which can be informally investigated and analyzed. In this chapter you can learn about a historical, social, and cultural context for geometry, and examine some concepts and procedures involving geometry ideas.

Big Mathematical Ideas:

> problem-solving strategies, shape & space, congruence, similarity, verifying, conjecturing, generalizing, decomposing

NCTM Standards Links:

> **K - 4:** Mathematics as problem solving; Mathematics as communication; Mathematics as reasoning; Mathematical connections; Geometry & spatial sense

> **5 - 8:** Mathematics as problem solving; Mathematics as communication; Mathematics as reasoning; Mathematical connections; Geometry

Chapter Outline:

> Historical/Social/Cultural Notes about Geometry
> Explanations Concerning Geometry
>> *Section 9.1*   Definitions
>> *Section 9.2*   Theorems and Postulates
> Bibliography

Historical/Social/Cultural Notes about Geometry

Geometry is probably one of the areas of mathematics whose development is exceptionally well documented in historical accounts of the subject. It is also one of the areas to which many civilizations in the world have contributed in some way. Thus, the geometry studied today in high schools and colleges has emerged as a result of a rich variety of cultural contributions, each of which added to the subject and helped to shape its present character. The word "geometry" itself comes from two Greek words, "geo" meaning earth, and "metry" meaning measure, suggesting that, initially, this field of study may have been related to and used for measuring land. Today, it has evolved into a field that involves the study of shapes, angles, mensuration, surfaces and solids.

The Egyptians are credited with two major achievements in geometry: the approximation of the area of the circle, and the derivations of a rule to calculate the volume of a truncated pyramid (that is, essentially a pyramid whose top has been cut off). The calculation of the area of the circle depended on an implicit value of π.

The Babylonians' achievements in the field of geometry are not regarded as highly as the Egyptians. Nevertheless, they had some remarkable accomplishments to their credit. They were not only successful in calculating the area of such shapes as rectangles, certain triangles and trapezoids, but evidence from their civilization suggests that they knew and could use the Pythagorean theorem, and had also done some work on similar triangles. Their work in these areas preceded similar work in the Greek civilization by about a thousand years!

In fact, the Pythagorean theorem was known to other civilizations as well, including the Chinese and the Hindu civilizations. The Chinese made successive use of the theorem to find the perimeter of polygons of 24,756 sides, thus calculating the value of π to about six digits! It remained the most accurate value of π for approximately a thousand years. The Hindus also made much use of the Pythagorean theorem in many practical ways. They also used geometric methods to calculate approximately the value of $\sqrt{2}$. They also knew some elementary trigonometry.

The Greek achievements in geometry were marked by enormous personal contributions by some of the ancient giants of mathematics. Zeno (whose famous paradox is mentioned in Chapter 7 on real numbers) and Eudoxus, who lived in the 4th century B.C., were two of the earliest ones. A third, Archimedes (287 - 212 B.C.), is regarded as one of the greatest mathematicians that ever lived. In fact, only two other mathematicians, Newton and Gauss, are regarded by mathematicians to be his intellectual peers. Various episodes from Archimedes' life have been documented in historical accounts. One story, in particular, describing his discovery of the first law of hydrostatics, is very well-known. It is said that once the king of Syracuse, where Archimedes lived, asked him to find a method to determine whether the crown made for him by his goldsmith was actually made of pure gold. Archimedes wrestled with this problem and one day, while he was in his bath, discovered the solution and gave the principle that goes by his name. The story goes on to say that Archimedes who was very excited by his discovery, jumped from his bath and ran down the streets of Syracuse, stark naked, shouting "Eureka! (I have found it)." The exclamation has since passed into the English language as a phrase marking any great discovery.

Archimedes' accomplishments in the field of mathematics are too numerous to relate in this short space. But among them was the relationship between the circumference and area of a circle, calculation of the volumes of a sphere, a cylinder and a cone, and methods of indirect proof such as proof by contradiction and exhaustion of possibilities. While many of these results may seem trivial today, for the times in which Archimedes lived, they were phenomenal. Some historians estimate that they marked the work of a person who was ahead of his time by as many as 2000 years!

While Archimedes' brilliance outshone the work of many of his contemporaries, another name that must be mentioned in connection with any historical account of geometry is that of Euclid, who is believed to have lived about 300 B.C. Two of Euclid's chief accomplishments will be mentioned here, the first of which is the systematic account that he gave of all the geometry that was known at his time in thirteen books (a part of which is now studied as algebra), collectively titled the *Elements*. In this book, Euclid stated definitions, postulates and axioms upon which what is now called Euclidean geometry is based. Euclid's second and in some ways, more important accomplishment was his realization that the fifth of his postulates was actually an assumption. The parallel postulate, as the fifth postulate came to be called acquired an independent status among the postulates. The negation of this postulate, surprisingly led to a whole new system of geometry that was labeled as non-Euclidean geometry.

Another interesting and historic moment in the development of geometry took place when this fifth postulate was challenged by a Russian mathematician, Lobachevsky (1792 - 1856). By challenging and rejecting this postulate, Lobachevsky created another set of postulates that were perfectly consistent and led to an entirely new kind of geometry. Unlike Euclidean geometry, this geometry was not on a flat surface. In fact, it was based on a spherical surface, and thus could be used to model geometry on the surface of the earth. By the creation of this geometry, Lobachevsky had succeeded in overturning a belief that had been regarded as absolute truth since the time of Euclid, nearly 2000 years before Lobachevsky! His success later prompted the creation of other kinds of non-Euclidean geometries that have proved very useful in studying different kinds of phenomena in modern times.

The study of geometry has always an important part of the curriculum in school mathematics. In fact, in recent years, there has been much attention on the teaching of geometry, and methods of teaching it. It may interest you to know that this interest in teaching is not entirely new. In 1905, a book entitled "First Book of Geometry" was published by Grace Young, an English mathematician of considerable brilliance who studied at Cambridge. Surprisingly, some of the ideas in the book appear to be relevant even today. In the book, Young critiqued the lack of attention paid to solid geometry as compared to two-dimensional geometry, and suggested that students would find it easier to understand three-dimensional geometry, which is a truer model of the real world. She also included in her book several diagrams that students could cut and fold to help them visualize the theorems they could study in three-dimensional geometry.

More recently, a Dutch couple, the van Hieles have become famous for a five-stage model of learning that they suggested to help students understand geometric concepts in a meaningful way. Their model, published in 1959, proceeds from level 0, a visual or holistic reasoning level, to level 4, where students can reason with all the rigor and formalization of modern mathematics. Their model had been the basis of change in the geometry curriculum in the former Soviet Union. It has also aroused considerable interest in other countries, including the United States, that are now trying to introduce reform in mathematics curriculum.

To end this note, we would like to present a surface that has been an object of much interest—the Mobius strip. To construct this surface, take a long strip of paper, twist it once, and then bring the edges of the strip together and tape them to form a twisted loop. Place a pencil anywhere on the strip and draw a continuous line along the middle of the strip. Now take a pair of scissors and cut along the line you drew. Repeat these two steps with the new loop that you get. Each time, share your findings with others. Try and find some other interesting features of this surface.

Explanations Concerning Geometry

Sections 9.1—Definitions

The definitions that we give here are working definitions of these terms as opposed to the formal definitions that you come across in most textbooks. They are intended to help you understand what the concept is in order to help you work with them.

Ray: A ray is a collection of points all of which lie on a line, that continues indefinitely in one direction. We shall call the point where the ray starts its endpoint.

Example 1: Rays AB, CD, and EF are shown below.

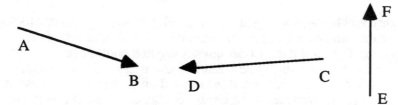

Angle: An angle is formed when two rays join together at their endpoint. An angle measures the inclination between two objects.

Example 2: The following figures represent two angles, labeled as angles ABC and PQR respectively. The points B and Q are called the vertices of the respective angles.

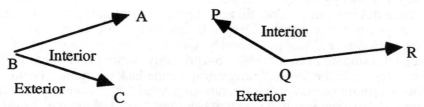

We notice that an angle divides a plane into two parts; we shall call these parts the interior and the exterior of the angle respectively.

Adjacent angles: Angles that are in the same plane that share a common ray are called adjacent angles. While the angles will have a common ray and will have the same vertex, their interiors will not intersect.

Example 3: The pair of angles ABC and CBD shown below are adjacent angles.

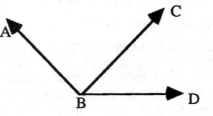

Complementary angles: Two angles whose sum is 90 degrees are called complementary angles.

Example 4: The angles PQR and XYZ are complementary angles.

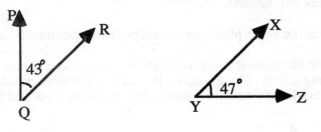

Supplementary angles: Two angles whose sum is 90 degrees are called supplementary angles.

Example 5: The angles LMN and RST are supplementary angles.

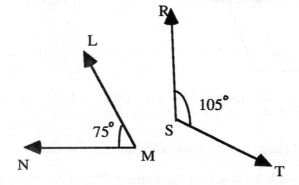

Vertical angles: Suppose AB and CD are two lines that intersect at a point O. The pair of angles AOD and COB are then said to form vertical angles.

Example 6: As one can see from the picture below, the pairs of angles AOC and DOB form another pair of vertical angles. A pair of vertical angles are always equal.

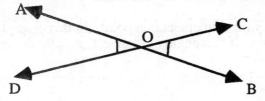

Collinear points: Points that lie on the same line are called collinear points.

Example 7: In the following pictures, the points P, M, and A are collinear points. Similarly, R and B are collinear points, and so are S and T. However, S, T and A, or T, P and M are not collinear points.

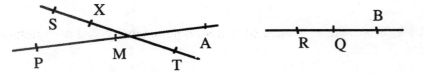

It is important to note that given any two points in a plane, they will always be collinear (since you can always draw a line between any two points).

Coplanar points: Points that lie in the same plane are called coplanar points.

<u>Example 8</u>: Consider the following picture—it is supposed to be a three dimensional picture that shows two planes intersecting along a line. The points A, B, and C are coplanar points. Similarly, the points P and Q are coplanar points. However, the points A, P, S and B are not coplanar.

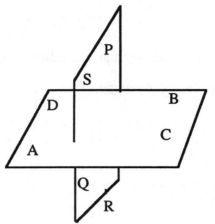

It is important to note that any three points in space are always coplanar.

Parallel and perpendicular lines: If you have any two lines in a plane, these lines must either intersect at one point or they will never meet. (Of course, the third possibility is that the lines lie on top of each other, but we shall disregard this trivial case.) If the two lines do not meet each other, no matter how far they are extended, then they are said to be parallel. The distance between such lines is always constant.

<u>Example 9</u>: The lines AB and CD shown below are parallel to each other.

If two lines in a plane are not parallel, then they must intersect in a point. In this case, the two lines meet at an angle at the point of intersection. If this angle of intersection is 90 degrees, then the lines are said to be perpendicular to each other.

Example 10: The lines PQ and XY shown below are perpendicular to each other.

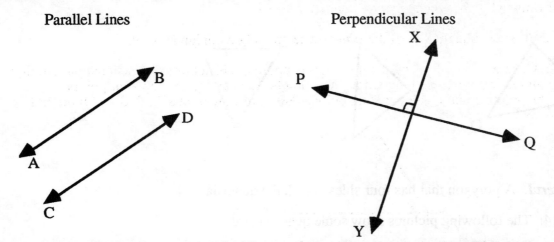

Parallel Lines   Perpendicular Lines

Polygon: A closed curve composed of line segments that starts and ends at the same point without crossing or retracing itself anywhere in its path is called a polygon. The word has two parts, poly- meaning many, and -gon, meaning angle.

Example 11: The figures ABCDE and PQRS show two polygons.

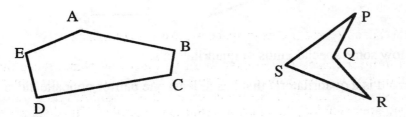

Regular polygon: If all the sides in a polygon are congruent, and all the angles in a polygon are congruent, then the polygon is called a regular polygon.

Example 12: The following pictures show regular polygons.

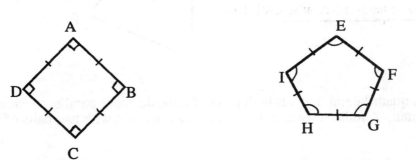

Triangle: A triangle is a polygon that has three sides. If all the three sides and the three angles are equal, the triangle is called an equilateral triangle. A triangle that has one right angle in it is called a right triangle. Other triangles that have special properties are also given special names.

<u>Example 13</u>: The following figures show some triangles.

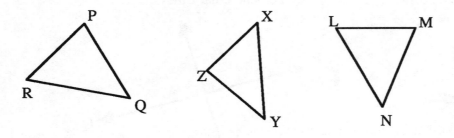

Quadrilateral: A polygon that has four sides is called a quadrilateral.

<u>Example 14</u>: The following pictures show some quadrilaterals.

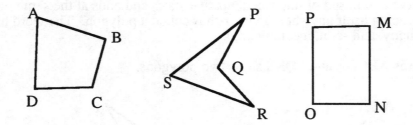

We shall discuss below some special kinds of quadrilaterals.

Trapezoid: A trapezoid is a quadrilateral that has at least one pair of opposite sides parallel to each other.

<u>Example 15</u>: The following pictures show two trapezoids.

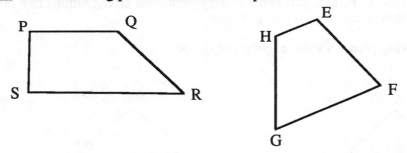

Parallelogram: A quadrilateral that has both pairs of opposite sides parallel to each other is called a parallelogram. Another way to think of it is as a trapezoid with two pairs of sides parallel.

Example 16: Two parallelograms are shown below.

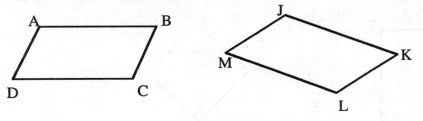

Rhombus: A rhombus is a quadrilateral whose opposite sides are parallel to each other, and all of whose sides are equal. Another way to think of it is as a parallelogram all whose sides are equal.

Example 17: The following pictures show some rhombi.

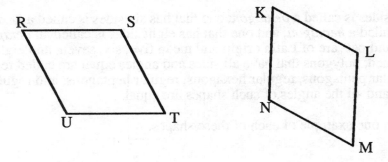

Rectangle: A rectangle is a parallelogram, all of whose angles are 90 degrees.

Example 18: The following pictures show some rectangles.

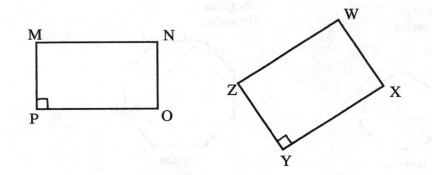

Square: A square is a rectangle all of whose sides are equal. The following are examples of squares. Another way to think about a square is to think of it as a rhombus, all of whose angles are 90 degrees.

<u>Example 19</u>: Some squares are shown below.

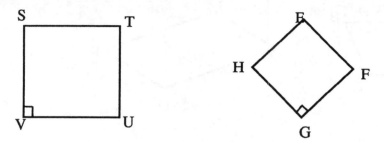

Pentagon, hexagon, heptagon, and octagon: The triangles and quadrilaterals are the geometric figures that are discussed the most in school geometry. However, there are other polygons that occur quite frequently in the world around us. We shall now define some of them.

A polygon that has five sides is called a *pentagon*; one that has six sides is called a *hexagon*; one that has seven sides is called a *heptagon*, and one that has eight sides is called an *octagon*. The prefixes pent-, hex-, hept-, and oct- are of Latin origin and mean five, six, seven, and eight respectively. As we mentioned, polygons that have all sides and angles equal are called regular polygons. We thus get regular pentagons, regular hexagons, regular heptagons, and regular octagons when all the sides and all the angles of such shapes are equal.

<u>Example 20</u>: Given below is one example of each of these shapes.

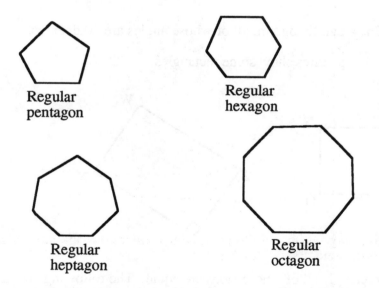

Regular
pentagon

Regular
hexagon

Regular
heptagon

Regular
octagon

Concave and convex polygons: These terms refer to the interior of a polygon. If a line joining any two points inside a polygon lies completely within the polygon, we say it is convex. Otherwise the polygon is said to be concave.

Example 21: Given below are examples of some convex and concave polygons. Line segments joining two points inside the polygon are shown to make the definitions clear.

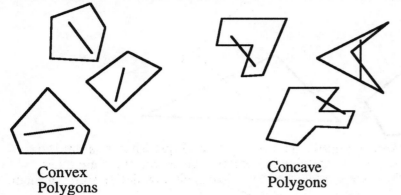

Convex
Polygons

Concave
Polygons

Congruent polygons: Two polygons are said to be congruent if when we superimpose one upon the other, the two polygons coincide completely. Thus, two congruent polygons are equal in all respects, that is, their corresponding sides and angles are equal to each other.

Example 22: Here are some examples of congruent pairs of figures. Figures 1 and 2 are congruent, as are 3 and 4.

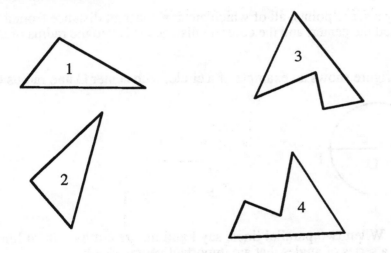

Similar polygons: Two polygons are said to be similar if their corresponding sides are proportional and their corresponding angles are equal.

<u>Example 23</u>: Some examples of similar polygons are given below.

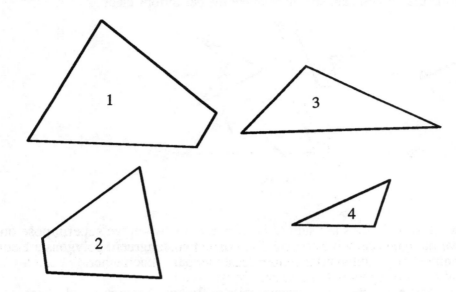

The pairs of figures 1 and 2 are similar, and so are 3 and 4.

Circle: A circle is formed by a set of points, all of which are at a constant distance from a fixed point. The fixed point is called the center, and the constant distance is called the radius of the circle.

<u>Example 24</u>: The following figure shows an example of a circle, with center O and radius OP.

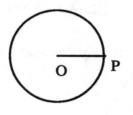

Lines cut by a transversal: When two parallel lines, say l and m, are cut by a third line, say n called the transversal, we get a series of angles that are important geometrically.

Example 25: Consider the figure below.

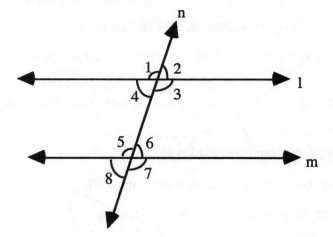

Pairs of angles like the ones formed by 1 and 5 are called ***corresponding angles***. They are in the same position on the lines l and m relative to n. Another pair of corresponding angles is given by the pair 4 and 8. Corresponding angles are always equal.

Pairs of angles like the ones formed by 4 and 6 are called ***alternate interior angles***. Another pair of corresponding angles is given by the pair 3 and 5. Such angles are always equal.

Pairs of angles like the ones formed by 4 and 5 are called ***interior angles***. Another pair of corresponding angles is given by the pair 3 and 6. Such angles are always supplementary.

Pairs of angles like the ones formed by 1 and 5 are called ***alternate exterior angles***. Another pair of corresponding angles is given by the pair 1 and 7. Such angles are always equal.

Section 9.2—Theorems and Postulates
Listed below are some theorems and postulates that you may find useful when proving various statements in the activities, and exercises and problems.

Lines and Angles
- Supplements of congruent angles are congruent.

- Complements of congruent angles are congruent.

- Vertical angles formed by intersecting lines are congruent.

- *Euclidean Parallel Postulate*: Given a line and a point, P, not on the line, there is exactly one line through P parallel to the given line.

- If two lines are cut by a transversal and alternate interior angles are equal, then the lines are parallel.

- If two lines are cut by a transversal and alternate exterior angles are equal, then the lines are parallel.

- If two lines are cut by a transversal and corresponding angles are equal, then the lines are parallel.

- If two parallel lines are cut by a transversal, then alternate interior angles are equal.

- If two parallel lines are cut by a transversal, then alternate exterior angles are equal.

- If two parallel lines are cut by a transversal, then corresponding angles are equal.

- If two lines are parallel to the same line, they are parallel to each other.

Triangles
- Pythagorean Theorem: If a right triangle has legs of length a and b and hypotenuse of length c, then $c^2 = a^2 + b^2$.

- In a triangle, angles opposite congruent sides are congruent.

- In a triangle, sides opposite congruent angles are congruent.

- Corresponding parts of congruent triangles are congruent.

- In any triangle, the line segment joining the midpoints of two sides of a triangle is parallel to the third side.

- In any triangle, the line segment joining the midpoints of two sides of a triangle is equal to half the third side.

- *Angle-Side-Angle Congruence Postulate (ASA):* If two angles and the included side of one triangle are congruent to two angles and the included side of another triangle, then the triangles are congruent.

- *Side-Angle-Side Congruence Postulate (SAS):* If two sides and the included angle of one triangle are congruent to two sides and the included angle of another triangle, then the triangles are congruent.

- *Side-Side-Side Congruence Theorem (SSS):* If three sides of one triangle are congruent to three sides of another triangle, then the two triangles are congruent.

- *Angle-Angle-Side Theorem (AAS):* If two angles and the side opposite one of them in one triangle are congruent to the corresponding parts of another triangle, then the two triangles are congruent.

- *Angle-Angle Similarity Theorem:* If two angles of one triangle are congruent to two angles of another triangle, then the two triangles are similar.

- *Side-Angle-Side Similarity Theorem (SAS):* If an angle of one triangle is congruent to an angle of another triangle and the sides including these angles are proportional, then the triangles are similar.

Quadrilaterals
- Opposite sides of a parallelogram are congruent.

- If both pairs of opposite sides of a quadrilateral are congruent, then the quadrilateral is a parallelogram.

Bibliography

Arithmetic Teacher. (1990, February). Focus issue on spatial sense, *37*.

Bright, G. W., & Harvey, J. G. (1988). Learning and fun with geometry games. *Arithmetic Teacher, 35,* 22-26.

Bruni, V., & Seidenstein, R. B. (1990). Geometric concepts and spatial sense In J. N. Payne (Ed.), *Mathematics for the young child* (pp 203-207). Reston, VA: National Council of Teachers of Mathematics.

Cangelosi, J. S. (1985). A "fair" way to discover circles. *Arithmetic Teacher, 33,* 11 - 13.

Carroll, W. M. (1988). Cross sections of clay solids. *Arithmetic Teacher, 35, 6-11.*

Chazan, D. (1990). "mplementing the *Standards*: Students' microcomputer-aided exploration in geometry. *Mathematics Teacher, 83,* 628-635.

Clements, D. C. & Battista. M. (1986). Geometry and geometric measurement." *Arithmetic Teacher, 33, 29-32.*

Craine, T. V. & N. Rubenstein, R. N. (1993). A quadrilateral hierarchy to facilitate learning in geometry. *Mathematics Teacher, 86* , 30-36.

Dana, M. E. (1987). Geometry: A square deal for elementary teachers. In M. M Lindquist (Ed.), *Learning and teaching geometry K-12* (pp. 113-125). Reston, VA: National Council of Teachers of Mathematics.

Del Grande, J. (1993). *Geometry and spatial sense: Addenda series, grades K-6.* Reston, VA: National Council of Teachers of Mathematics.

Ellington, B. (1983). Star Trek: A construction problem using compass and straightedge. *Mathematics Teacher, 76,* 329-332.

Evered, L. J. (1992). Folded fashions: Symmetry in clothing design. *Arithmetic Teacher, 40,* 204-206.

Flores, A. (1993) Pythagoras meets van Hiele. *School* Science and Mathematics, 93, 152-157.

Fuys, D J, & Liebov, A K. (1993). Geometry and spatial sense In R J Jensen (Ed.), *Research ideas for the classroom: Early childhood mathematics* (pp 195-222) Old Tappan, NJ: Macmillan.

Geddes, D. (1992). *Geometry in the middle grades. Addenda series, grades 5-8.* Reston. VA: National Council of Teachers of Mathematics.

Hill, J. M. (Ed.) (1987). *Geometry for grades K-6: Readings from The Arithmetic Teacher.* Reston, VA. National Council of Teachers of Mathematics.

Hoffer, A. R., & Hoffer, S. A. K. (1992). Geometry and visual thinking. In T R. Post (Ed.), *Teaching mathematics in grades K-8: Research-based methods* (2nd ed.) (pp. 249-277). Needham Heights, MA: Allyn & Bacon.

Johnson, A., & Boswell, L. (1992). Geographic constructions. *Mathematics Teacher, 85,* 184-187.

Krause, E. F. (1986). *Taxicab geometry: An adventure in non-Euclidean geometry.* New York: Dover Publications, Inc.

Kriegler, S. (1991). The Tangram: It's more than an ancient puzzle. *Arithmetic Teacher, 38,* 38-43.

Lappan, G. & Even, R. (1988). Similarity in the middle grades. *Arithmetic Teacher, 35,* 32-35.

Lappan, G., Phillips, E. A., & Winter, M. J. (1984). Spatial visualization. *Mathematics Teacher 77,* 618-625.

Masingila, J. O. (1993). Secondary geometry: A lack of evolution. *School Science and Mathematics, 93* (1), 38-44.

Morrow, L. J. (1991). Implementing the *Standards*: Geometry through the *Standards*. *Arithmetic Teacher, 38,* 21 -25.

Nowlin, D. (1993). Practical geometry problems: The case of the Ritzville pyramids. *Mathematics Teacher, 86,* 198-200.

Rowan, T. E. (1990). Implementing the *Standards*: The geometry standards in K-8 mathematics. *Arithmetic Teacher, 37,* 24-28.

Rubenstein, R. N., Lappan, G., Phillips, E., & Fitzgerald, W. (1993). Angle sense: A valuable connector. *Arithmetic Teacher, 40,* 352-358.

Rubenstein. R. N., & Thompson, D R. (1995). Making connections with transformations in grades K-8. In P. A. House (Ed). Connecting mathematics across the curriculum (pp. 65-78). Reston, VA: National Council of Teachers of Mathematics.

Thiessen, D. & Matthias, M. (1989). Selected children's books for geometry. *Arithmetic Teacher, 37,* 47-51.

Wilson, P. S. (1990). Understanding angles: Wedges to degrees. *Mathematics Teacher, 83,* 294-300.

Winter, J J., Lappan, G., Phillips, E., & Fitzgerald, W. (1986). *Middle grades mathematics project: Spatial visualization.* Menlo Park, CA: Addison-Wesley.

Woodward, E., Gibbs, V., & Shoulders, M. (1992). A fifth-grade similarity unit. *Arithmetic Teacher, 39,* 22-26.

Yeshurun, S. (1985). An improvement of the congruent angles theorem. *Mathematics Teacher, 78,* 53-54.

Chapter 10: Measurement

Chapter Overview:

Perhaps no part of mathematics is more clearly applicable to everyday life than measurement. As a consequence of the practicality of measurement in the real world, it is a very important strand in the elementary school mathematics curriculum. In particular, students learn extremely useful measurement skills (e.g., how to use a ruler), concepts (e.g., the concepts of area and perimeter), and key formulas (e.g., $A = l \cdot w$). Just as important is the fact that making measurements can be a source of many, very interesting problems. For example, did you know that two shapes can have the same perimeter, but different areas? One natural question that follows from this is can two shapes have the same area, but different perimeters? In this chapter you can learn about a historical, social, and cultural context for measurement, and examine some concepts and procedures involving measurement ideas.

Big Mathematical Ideas:

> problem-solving strategies, conjecturing; verifying; generalizing

NCTM Standards Links:

> *K - 4:* Mathematics as problem solving; Mathematics as communication; Mathematics as reasoning; Mathematical connections; Measurement

> *5 - 8:* Mathematics as problem solving; Mathematics as communication; Mathematics as reasoning; Mathematical connections; Measurement

Chapter Outline:

Historical/Social/Cultural Notes about Measurement

One of the oldest forms of human mathematical activity is measuring. Just as humans developed numeration systems to record and communicate quantities, they also needed methods of measuring quantities such as time, length, and weight. Over time people needed ways to measure such quantities as volume, capacity, temperature, speed, noise, fuel consumption, electric current, density, light intensity, efficiency and so on. We will discuss the historical development of several of these methods of measuring.

Measuring Time

Historical records indicate that time was one of the first quantities that humans measured. Thousands of years ago, people created ways to finding the number of days in a year. The Babylonians divided the day into 12 hours and the night into 12 hours over 3,000 years ago. Their system, however, had flexible hour lengths, with shorter day hours and longer night hours during the winter. The Greeks, at some point, decided to divide the day and night into 24 equal time periods, but it was not until around 1330 that the hour was standardized. Now, an hour at any point of the year was equal to an hour at any other time of the year; furthermore, an hour at one location of the earth was equal to an hour at another location.

The Babylonians also thought that there were 360 days in a year, and divided a circle into 360 equal parts. This is how we have come to measure angles, in terms of *degrees* where each degree is 1/360 of a circle.

The earliest known instrument for measuring time is the sundial and comes from Egypt from around 1500 B.C. The water clock was developed about 1400 B.C. to overcome the limitations of the sundial (e.g., could not be used at night or on cloudy days). The hourglass was developed about 300 B.C., and the sand clock was another instrument used to measure time in the 1400s. In the 1700s the mechanical watch was accurate enough and inexpensive enough to be used outside of scientific experiments.

Measuring Length

Throughout history, humans have chosen various units for measure length or distance. The earliest recorded linear unit of measurement is the cubic, the distance from the point of the elbow to the outstretched tip of the middle finger. Foot was another early unit of measure, and its length was likely based on the length of King Charlemagne's foot. In the 10th century, King Edgar I decreed that the yard would be the distance from the tip of his nose to the top of the middle finger of his outstretched arm. This decree was to regulate trade in textiles, so that one yard of cloth would be the same throughout England.

The Romans divided one foot into 12 equal units, called unciae from which we got our word inch. The Romans also had a unit called pace, where one pace was equal to five feet (i.e., the distance between a right step and a left step). Another Roman unit was milia passuum (mile) which was equal to 1,000 paces. What connection do you see between the Roman mile and our mile?

Measuring Weight (Mass)

The barleycorn and the seed of the carob plant (from which the word carat comes for measuring gold and diamonds) are two ancient units for measuring weight. Three different systems of weights evolved over the centuries: the avoirdupois system for everyday use, the troy system to weigh precious metals and gems, and the apothecary system for very small amounts. In the U.S. customary system, weight is measured in avoirdupois units such as tons, pounds, and ounces. One pound (lb) equals 16 ounces (oz) and 2000 lb equals 1 ton.

Measuring Volume and Capacity

Over time, two related systems of measure for volume developed, depending on whether the quantity being measured was dry or wet. For dry volume, some units that were used include ounce, pint, quart, peck, and bushel. For liquid volume, the units included jigger, jack, jill, cup, pint, quart, pottle, gallon, pail, peck, bushel, cask, barrel, and pipe. Today, we still use some of these units. For dry volume, some of our units are cubic foot, cubic yard, cubic inch. For liquid volume, we use cup, pint, quart, and gallon.

Measuring Temperature

Gabriel Fahrenheit, a German instrument maker, made the first mercury thermometer—for measuring temperature—in 1714. He labeled the lowest temperature that he could create in his laboratory as 0° and the normal temperature of the body as 98°. Other designated points on his scale include the freezing point of water at 32° and the boiling point of water at 212°.

We will now examine the metric system and see how some of these quantities are measured with metric units.

The Metric System

Gabriel Mouton, a Frenchman, proposed the idea of a system of measures based on powers of 10 in 1670. The metric system developed over the next hundred years as scientists and other people made various proposals for a uniform system of measurement. Before this time, there was no uniform system, and there were thousands of different systems being used around the world. Even more troubling was the fact that even within one system, there was not uniformity in the units, so that a pint in one location was not equivalent to a pint in another location. In 1793, the French Academy of Sciences proposed a new metric system for all units of measurement. Today, the United States is one of only a few countries that has not adopted the metric system.

The metric system is based on a standard unit (for length, mass, volume) with prefixes for multiples of the unit and fractions of the unit. The following prefixes are used with the multiple or fraction shown in parentheses: milli (1/1,000), centi (1/100), deci (1/10), deca (10), hecto (100), kilo (1,000). The standard unit of length in the metric system is the meter, while for mass the standard unit is the gram, and for volume/capacity the standard unit is the liter.

In 1742, Anders Celsius, a Swedish astronomer, proposed a modification in the units of measurement used by the Fahrenheit system. He suggested that the reference points be the freezing point of water (0°) and the boiling point of water (100°). This metric temperature system is called the Celsius system, or the centigrade system (100 grades).

Coordinate Geometry

One of the most important developments in the study of metric geometry took place when geometry was linked to algebra, creating a branch of mathematics called coordinate geometry. In one stroke, this event changed the face of geometry forever. It made modern geometry possible. The credit for this remarkable achievement goes to a French mathematician, Rene Descartes (1596 - 1650).

The basic principles of Cartesian geometry, as it is often referred to after its inventor, is very simple. The method consists of laying down two lines, intersecting each other at right angles. These lines are called the axes, and the point at which they intersect, the origin. Given this basic framework, one can locate any point on the entire plane with no other reference except the relative position of the point with regard to these two lines. This reference is established by giving the coordinates of the point in the form of a number pair (x, y), where x represents the location of the point in the east-west direction, and y the location in the north-south direction. The process is very similar to locating an address in any American city, where roads often form a grid system running either parallel or perpendicular to each other.

After establishing this system of coordinates, Descartes showed that if there is a set of points that lie on a curve on the coordinate plane, one can connect all the coordinates of the points through an algebraic equation. This simple form of establishing a connection between geometry and algebra revolutionized the study of conic sections, such as parabolas, circles, ellipses, and hyperbolas.

Explanations Concerning Measurement

Section 10.1—Planar Geometry Definitions and Formulas

In this section, we shall discuss geometrical shapes that lie on a plane, such as rectangles, triangles, parallelograms and trapezoids.

Perimeter: The perimeter of a planar shape is the total length of its boundaries. For a polygon, the perimeter is the total length of its sides. For some shapes, we can develop formulas that are useful in calculating the their perimeter quickly.

Area of a planar shape: The area of a planar shape is the total region enclosed by the shape. Once again, there are formulas that help to recall the area of certain shapes quite quickly. We give these below as well.

- Perimeter of a rectangle with sides of length a and b = 2(a + b)

- Area of a rectangle with sides of length a and b = ab

- Perimeter of a parallelogram with sides of length a and b = 2(a + b)

- Area of a parallelogram with base of length b, and height h = bh

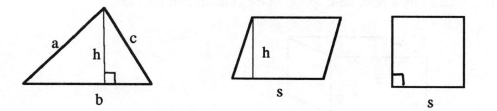

- Perimeter of a triangle with sides of length a, b and c = a + b + c

- Area of a triangle with base of length b and height h = 1/2 bh

- Perimeter of a rhombus with sides of length s = 4s

- Area of a rhombus with sides of length s, and height h = hs

- Perimeter of a square with sides of length s = 4s

- Area of a square with sides of length s = s^2

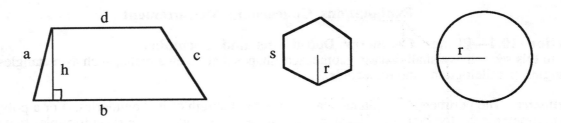

- Perimeter of a trapezoid with sides of length a, b, c, and d = a + b + c + d

- Area of a trapezoid with parallel sides of length a and b, and height h = 1/2 (a + b)h

- Perimeter of a regular polygon of n sides with sides of length s = ns

- Area of a regular polygon of n sides with sides of length s and radial distance r = 1/2 rns

- Circumference (perimeter) of a circle with radius r = $2\pi r$

- Area of a circle with radius r = πr^2

Section 10.2—Solid Geometry Definitions and Formulas

In this section, we shall discuss terms related to geometrical shapes in three dimensions, such as spheres, cylinders, and cones. The two physical quantities often related to such shapes are their surface area and volume.

Surface Area: The surface area of a solid figure is the total area of its external surfaces.

Volume: The volume of a solid geometrical shape is a measure of its capacity or the amount of space that the figure encloses.

We give below the formulas to calculate the surface area and volume of certain geometrical shape. The formulas are preceded by a brief description of the solid and its picture.

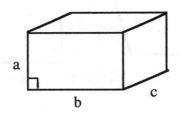

Figure 10.1

Right rectangular prism (Figure 10.1): A right rectangular prism is formed by joining three pairs of congruent rectangles along their edges in such a way that each of the six rectangles is joined all but one of the other four along its edges.

- Surface area of a right rectangular prism with sides of length a, b, and c = 2(ab + ac + bc)

- Volume of a right rectangular prism with sides of length a, b, and c = abc

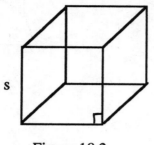

Figure 10.2

Cube (Figure 10.2): A cube is a right rectangular prism all whose faces are congruent.

- Surface area of a cube with sides of length s = $6s^2$

- Volume of a cube with sides of length s= s^3

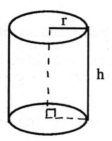

Figure 10.3

Right circular cylinder (Figure 10.3): A circular cylinder is formed by taking two congruent circles in two parallel planes and joining the circumference of the two circles by line segments. In a right circular cylinder the line joining the centers of the two circles is perpendicular to the each of the planes in which the circles lie.

- Surface area of a right circular cylinder with radius of the circular base r and height h = $2\pi r^2 + 2\pi rh$

- Volume of a right circular cylinder with radius of the circular base r and height h = $\pi r^2 h$

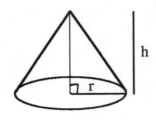

Figure 10.4

Right circular cone (Figure 10.4): A circular cone is formed by taking a circle in a plane, called the base of the cone and joining every point on its circumference to a point not in the plane called its apex. In a right circular cone, the line joining the center of the base to the apex is perpendicular to the plane of the base.

- Surface area of a right circular cone with radius of the base r, and
  height $h = \pi r^2 + \pi r \sqrt{(h^2 + r^2)}$

- Volume of a right circular cone with radius of the base r, and height $h = 1/3 \, \pi r^2 h$

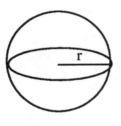

Figure 10.5

Sphere (Figure 10.5): A sphere is a three dimensional analog of a circle. It consists of all the points in space whose distance from a fixed point also in space is constant. The fixed point is called the center of the sphere and the constant distance is called the radius.

- Surface area of a sphere with radius $r = 4\pi r^2$

- Volume of a sphere with radius $r = 4/3 \, \pi r^3$

Section 10.3—Coordinate Geometry

This branch of metric geometry helps us study geometry with the help of algebra. You have already used this idea if you have completed activities in Chapter 7 and Chapter 8. We will only take a brief look at coordinate geometry here.

Coordinate geometry involves studying shapes by plotting points on a rectangular grid, called the Cartesian plane (named after Rene Descartes, mentioned in the historical notes). The plane consists of two perpendicular lines—one horizontal and the other vertical— intersecting each other at a point called the origin. The two lines are called the axes, the horizontal one being called the x axis, and the vertical one being called the y-axis. Both the axes are calibrated using positive and negative real numbers (often we need to use only the integers). The numbers on the right and on top of the origin are usually taken as positive and the ones to the left and below it are marked negative. Once we have set up this framework, we can use it to plot points on a line, in a region, or any other two-dimensional geometrical shape or object.

Here is an example of a rectangular grid with some points marked on it. We also include a line and a circle on the plane. The points marked are A with x coordinate 1, and y coordinate 2, usually written as (1, 2). Similarly, we can write P(–4, –3). The line CD joins the points C(4, 4) and D(1, –3). The circle in the top left corner has its center at (–4, 4) and a radius of 1 unit.

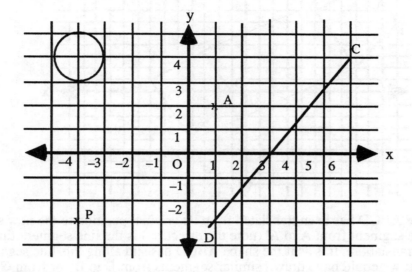

Slope of a line: The slope of a line is a measure of its inclination. We often define the slope of a line as its ride over run. This means that we choose any two points, say $P(x_1, y_1)$ and $Q(x_2, y_2)$ on the line. Then the slope of the line is defined as $(y_2 – y_1)/(x_2 – x_1)$. For the lione CD above, we may choose the points C(4, 4) and D(1, –3) as the points the line passes through. Then, the slope of the line will be equal to $(4 – (–3))/(4 – 1) = 7/3$. (As you can see, we may choose either of the two points as (x_1, y_1))

Section 10.4—Transformations

Geometrical shapes lend themselves to the idea of transformations that involve changing the position of the shape with regard to its original position some measurable way. In this section, we shall discuss three such transformations — translations, rotations, and reflections.

Translations: A translation is often seen as a sliding transformation. It involves sliding a geometrical shape along a line segment in one direction by some fixed amount. The line segment that helps to decide the magnitude and the direction of the transformation is regarded as a reference in such a transformation. In a translation, the position of any point in the original shape and its new position after the shape has been translated is described by this directed (as it has a direction) line segment.

For example, consider the shape below.

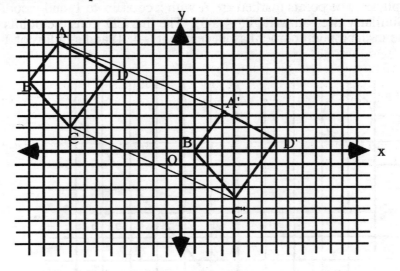

Here, the shape ABCD has been translated from its original position to the new shape, A'B'C'D'. The line segment from A to A' (note the direction) is the line segment that serves as a reference for this translation. It is as if the shape ABCD has slid along this line segment to its new position. Note that we could have drawn similar segments from B to B', or from C to C', or from D to D'. All such line segments would have been identical in magnitude and direction. Since the shape is on a grid, we can also quantify the translation with the help of the units on the grid. Thus, ABCD has moved 12 units to the right and 6 units below its original position as a result of the translation.

Rotation: A rotation is a transformation that moves a geometrical shape around a fixed point. The transformation is often see as a turning motion that rotates the original shape through a fixed angle. Consider the following example of a rotation.

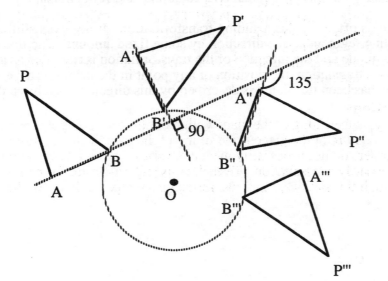

The picture above shows how the triangle PAB has been rotated around the point O. Triangle P'A'B' shows the triangle rotated through 90 degrees (as is marked by the angle between the bases of the two triangles); the next position P"A"B" shows the original triangle PAB rotated through an angle of 135 degrees (marked as the angle between the two bases); the last triangle P'''A'''B''' shows the triangle rotated through 180 degrees (the lines through the bases will now be parallel). Incidentally, you may note that O is the midpoint of the segment joining B and B'''. While we have drawn the lines through the bases, you may check the angles of rotation by drawing the lines through any of the three sides of the original triangle and the corresponding sides of the rotated triangle.

Reflection: A reflection is a transformation that flips a geometrical shape over a fixed line. Consider the following example.

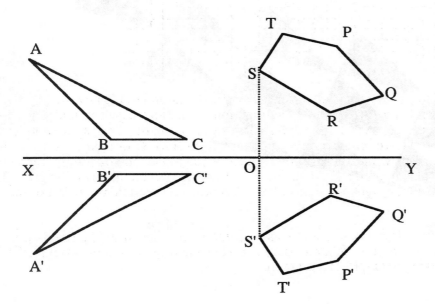

In the picture above, the triangle ABC has been reflected over the line XY to get the transformed image A'B'C'. Similarly, the pentagon PQRST has been reflected over XY to get the reflected image P'Q'R'S'T'. As you may note, the distance of the reflected image of each point from the line XY is the same as the distance of the point from the line. In other words, for example, the distance SO is the same as the distance S'O. We may drw similar correspondences between any point and its reflected image.

Section 10.5—Tessellations

A *tessellation* of the plane is the filling of the plane with repetitions of polygonal regions so that all corners meet at a vertex. A *tiling* of the plane is the filling of the plane with repetitions of polygonal regions where corners do not necessarily meet at a vertex. Thus, a tessellation is a tiling, but a tiling is not necessarily a tessellation. Tessellations and tilings are formed by transforming a figure—through translations, rotations, reflections—repeatedly to fill the plane.

Some examples of tessellations are shown below. The first one demonstrates how, through translations and rotations, it is possible to tessellate the plane with any triangle. The second figure demonstrates how a regular triangle can be rotated to tessellate the plane. The third example demonstrates how an irregular shape has been translated to tessellate the plane. The rectangular grid underlying the tessellation may provide you will an idea of how a tessellating tile (the template that is used to form the tessellation) can be formed from a rectangle by conserving area. How is a tessellation similar to an iterated function? How is it different?

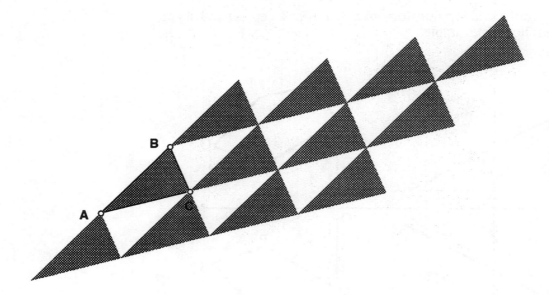

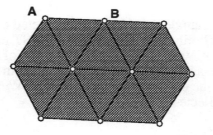

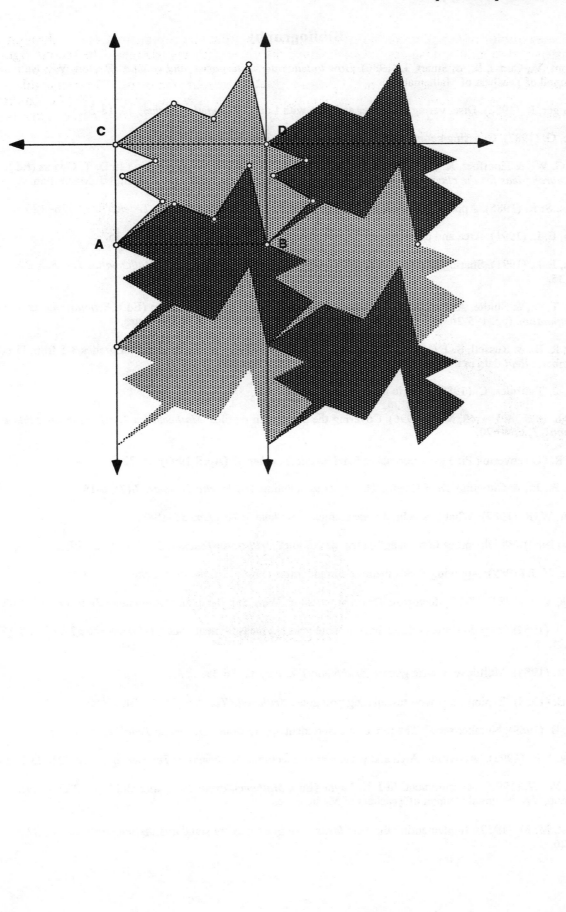

Bibliography

Beaumont, V., Curtis, R., & Smart, J. (1986). *How to teach perimeter, area, and volume.* Reston, VA: National Council of Teachers of Mathematics.

Binswanger, R. (1988). Discovering perimeter and area with Logo. *Arithmetic Teacher, 36,* 18-24.

Bledsoe, G. (1987). Guessing geometric shapes. *Mathematics Teacher, 80, 1 78-80.*

Bright, G. W., & Hoeffner. K. (1993). Measurement, probability, statistics, and graphing In D. T. Owens (Ed.), *Research ideas for the classroom: Middle grades mathematics* (pp. 7~98) Old Tappan, NJ: Macmillan.

Clemens, S. R. (1985). Applied measurement: Using problem solving. *Mathematics Teacher, 78,* 176- 180.

Clopton, E. L. (1991). Area and perimeter are independent. *Mathematics Teacher, 84,* 33-35.

Clopton, E. L. (1991). Sharing teaching ideas: Area and perimeter are independent. *Mathematics Teacher, 84,* 33-35.

Coburn, T. G., & Shulte, A. P. (1986). Estimation in measurement. In H. L. Schoen (Ed.), *Estimation and mental computation* (pp. 195-203) Reston, VA: National Council of Teachers of Mathematics.

Corwin, R. B., & Russell, S. J. (1990). Measuring: *From* paces to feet. (A unit of study for grades 3-5 from Used numbers: *Real* data in the *classroom)* Palo Alto, CA: Dale Seymour.

Fay, N., & Tsairides, C. (1989). Metric mall. *Arithmetic Teacher, 37,* 6- 11.

Fosnaugh, L. S., & Harrell, M E. (1996). Covering the plane with reptiles. *Mathematics Teaching in the Middle School, 1,* 666-670.

Gerver, R. "Discovering Pi: Two Approaches." *Arithmetic Teacher* 37 (April 1990): 18-22.

Giganti. P., Jr., & Cittadino, M. J (1990). The art of tessellation. *Arithmetic Teacher, 3I(7),* 6-16.

Harrison, W. R. (1987). What lies behind measurement? *Arithmetic Teacher, 34,* 19-21.

Hart, K. (1984). Which comes first - length, area, or volume? *Arithmetic Teacher, 31,* 16- 18, 26-27.

Hawkins, V. J. (1989). Applying Pick's theorem to randomized areas. *Arithmetic Teacher, 36,* 47-49.

Hawkins, V. J. (1984). The Pythagorean Theorem revisited: Weighing the results. *Arithmetic Teacher , 32,* 36-37.

Hiebert, J. (1984). Why do some children have trouble reaming measurement concepts? *Arithmetic Teacher, 31(7),* 19-24.

Jensen, R. (1984). Multilevel metric games. *Arithmetic Teacher, 32,* 36-39.

Kaiser, B. (1988). Explorations with tessellating polygons. *Arithmetic Teacher, 36,* 19-24.

Kastner, B. (1989). Number sense: The role of measurement applications. *Arithmetic Teacher, 36,* 40-46.

Kennedy, J. B. (1993). Activities: Area and perimeter connections. *Mathematics Teacher, 86,* 218-221, 23 1 -232.

Liedtke, W. W. (1990). Measurement. In J. N. Payne (Ed.), *Mathematics for the young* child (pp. 229—249). Reston, VA: National Council of Teachers of Mathematics.

Lindquist, M. M. (1989). Implementing the *Standards*: The measurement standards. *Arithmetic Teacher, 37,* 22-26.

Marche, M. M. (1984). A Pythagorean curiosity. *Mathematics Teacher, 77,* 611-613.

Masingila, J. O. (1995). Carpet laying: An illustration of everyday mathematics. In P.A. House (Ed.), *Connecting mathematics across the curriculum* (pp. 163-169), 1995 Yearbook of the National Council of Teachers of Mathematics. Reston, VA: National Council of Teachers of Mathematics.

McLaughlin, H. (1992). Activities: Determining area and calculating cost: A "model" application. *Mathematics Teacher, 85,* 360-361, 367-370.

Miller, L. D., & Miller, J. (1989). Metric week— The capitol way. *Mathematics Teacher, 82,* 454-458.

Miller, W. A., & Wagner, L. (1993). Activities: Pythagorean dissection puzzles. *Mathematics Teacher, 86,* 302-308, 313-314.

Neufeld, K. A. (1989). Body measurement. *Arithmetic Teacher, 36,* 12- 15.

Parker, J., & Widmer, C. C. (1993). Teaching mathematics with technology: Patterns in measurement. *Arithmetic Teacher, 40,* 292-295.

Renshaw, B. S. (1986). Symmetry the trademark way. *Arithmetic Teacher, 34,* 6-12.

Rhone, L. (1995). Measurement in a primary-grade integrated curriculum. In P. A. House (Ed.) *Connecting mathematics across the curriculum* (pp. 124-133). Reston, VA: National Council of Teachers of Mathematics.

Schultz, J. E. (1991). Area models: Spanning the mathematics of grades 3-9. *Arithmetic Teacher, 39,* 42-46.

Shaw, J. M (1983). Student-made measuring tools. *Arithmetic Teacher, 31*(3), 12- 15.

Shaw, J. M., & Cliatt, M. J. P. (1989). Developing measurement sense. In P. R. Trafton (Ed.), *New directions for elementary school mathematics* (pp. 149-155). Reston, VA: National Council of Teachers of Mathematics.

Smith, R. F. (1986). Let's do it: Coordinate geometry for third graders. *Arithmetic Teacher, 36,* 6- 11.

Souza, R. (1988). Golfing with a protractor. *Arithmetic Teacher, 35,* 52-56.

Szetela, W., & Owens, D. T. (1986). Finding the area of a circle: Use a cake pan and leave out the pi. *Arithmetic Teacher, 33*(9), 12-18.

Terc, M. (1985). Coordinate geometry: Art and mathematics. *Arithmetic Teacher, 33,* 22-24.

Thompson, C. S., & Van de Walle, J. A. (1985). Learning about rulers and measuring. *Arithmetic Teacher, 32*(8), 8-12.

Vissa, J. M. (1987). Coordinate graphing: Shaping a sticky situation. *Arithmetic Teacher, 35,* 6- 10.

Whitman, N. (1991). Activities: Line and rotational symmetry. *Mathematics Teacher, 84,* 296-302.

Wilson, P. S. & Adams, V. M. (1992). A dynamic way to teach angle and angle measure. *Arithmetic Teacher, 39,* 6-13.

Wilson, P. S., & Rowland, R. E. (1993). Teaching measurement In R. J. Jensen (Ed.), *Research ideas for the classroom: Early childhood mathematics* (pp. 171-194). Old Tappan, NJ. Macmillan.

Wilson. P. S., & Osbome, A. (1992). Foundational ideas in teaching about measure. In T. R. Post (Ed.), *Teaching mathematics in grades K-8: Research-based methods (*2nd ea.) (pp. 89-121). Needham Heights, MA: Allyn & Bacon.

Zaslavsky, C. (1990). Symmetry in American folk art. *Arithmetic Teacher, 38,* 6- 12.

Zweng, M. J (1986). Introducing angle measurement through estimation In H. L. Schoen (Ed.), *Estimation and mental computation* (pp 212-219). Reston, VA: National Council of Teachers of Mathematics.

Glossary

Additive: A numeration system is said to be additive if the value of the set of symbols representing a number is the sum of the values of the individual symbols.

Adjacent angles: Angles in a plane that share a common ray without their interiors intersecting are called adjacent angles.

Algorithm: A step-by-step procedure for performing a mathematical task.

Angle: An angle is formed when two rays join together at their endpoint.

Approximation: A result that is not exact, but sufficiently close for a given purpose. For instance, 22/7 may be used as an approximation for the value of pi.

Area of a planar shape: The area of a planar shape is the total region enclosed by the shape.

Arithmetic mean: The arithmetic mean of n numbers is their sum divided by n.

Associativity: A set is said to have the property of associativity under an operation * if for any three elements a, b, and c in it, a * (b * c) = (a * b) * c.

Average: A term widely used to refer to the arithmetic mean.

Bar graph: A graph, used to present frequency distributions or time series, which consists of bars (rectangles) of equal width, whose lengths are proportional to the frequencies (or values) they represent. A sample bar graph is shown below.

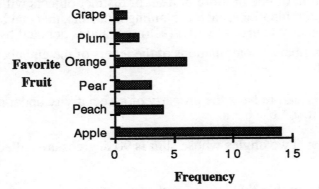

Base: A numeration system has a base if the numbers in that system reflect a process of repeated grouping by some number greater than one. The number is then called the base.

Box-and-whisker plot (or box plot): A graph that displays the *5-number summary* of a set of data. A box-and-whisker plot for the following 12 quiz scores (10 points was the maximum score) is shown below: 8, 4, 9, 10, 10, 5, 7, 3, 8, 2, 9, 7.

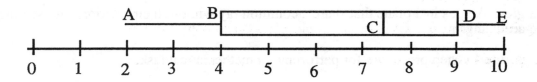

A -- lowest score;   B -- 1st quartile;   C -- 2nd quartile
D -- 3rd quartile;   E -- highest score

Central tendency or measure of central tendency: This expression is sometimes used to refer to statistics—such as the mean, median, or mode—which indicate the average value of a data set.

Circle: A circle is formed by a set of points, all of which are at a constant distance from a fixed point.

Closure: A set is said to be closed with respect to an operation * if, for any two elements a and b in it, a * b belongs to the set.

Collinear points: Points that lie on the same line are called collinear points.

Combination: A selection of one or more of a set of distinct objects without regard to order. The number of possible combinations, each containing k objects, that can be formed from a collection of n distinct objects is given by $(n!)/(k!)(n-k)!$ and is denoted by (n, k), ${}_nC_k$, $C(n, k)$, or C^n_k. For example, the number of combinations of the letters of the alphabet, taken four at a time, is $26!/4!(26-4)! = 14950$.

Commutativity: A set is said to have the property of associativity under an operation * if for any two elements a and b in it, a * b = b * a.

Complementary angles: Two angles whose sum is 90 degrees are called complementary angles.

Composite number: A number that has more than two factors.

Concave polygon: If every line joining any pair of two points inside a polygon does not lie completely within the polygon, we say it is concave.

Conditional probability: The probability that A will occur given that B has occurred or will occur. If A and B are any two events and the probability of B is not equal to zero, then the conditional probability of A relative to B is denoted P(A|B) and given by P(A&B)/P(B), where P(A&B) is the probability of the joint occurrence of A and B.

Congruence modulo m: A number a is said to be congruent to a number b modulo m if m divides the number $(a - b)$.

Congruent polygons: Two polygons are said to be congruent if, when we superimpose one upon the other, the two polygons coincide completely.

Convex polygon: If a line joining any two points inside a polygon lies completely within the polygon, we say it is convex.

Coplanar points: Points that lie in the same plane are called coplanar points.

Cube: A solid body consisting of six congruent squares joined together.

Data: The results of an experiment, census, survey, and any kind of process or operation.

Decimal: A decimal representation is a means of writing a fraction in the base ten place-value system.

Dependent events: (See Independent events).

Dependent variable: When considering the relationship between two variables, where the value of one *depends* on the value of the other, one of the variables is called a *dependent variable*, and the other is called an *independent variable*. For example, the number of apples you can purchase *depends* on the amount of money you have. In this situation, "number of apples" is a dependent variable, and "amount of money" is an independent variable.

Descriptive statistics: Any treatment of data which does not involve generalizations. (See Inferential Statistics).

Distribution: This term is used to refer to the over-all scattering of observed data. It is often used as a synonym for "frequency distribution."

Distributivity: Given a set with two operations, * and Σ, we say * distributes over Σ if, for any three elements, a, b and c in the set, $a * (b \Sigma c) = a * b \Sigma a * c$.

Divisible: A number, b, is said to be divisible by another number, a, if a is a factor of b. In other words, when b is divided b a, the remainder is 0.

Divisibility test for a number m: A quick and relatively easy method of determining if a given number is divisible by m without performing the actual division.

Divisor: A number, a, is said to be a divisor of another number, b, if a divides b without leaving a remainder.

Domain of a function: The set of all values that are allowed as input values of a function. For example, in the function

$$f(x) = \frac{1}{x-5}$$

all real numbers *except* 5 could be in the domain. 5 cannot be in the domain because

$$f(5) = \frac{1}{5-5} = \frac{1}{0}$$

is undefined.

Equivalent fractions: Two or more fractions in which if all common factors between the numerator and the denominator of each fraction are removed, the fractions are the same.

Even number: A number is said to be even if it is divisible by 2.

Event: An event, in probability theory, is a subset of a sample space (See Sample space). For example, the event of getting an odd number when a die is tossed is the subset {1, 3, 5} of the sample space {1, 2, 3, 4, 5, 6}.

Expanded notation (or form): A form of writing a number so as to represent the value of each digit using multiples of powers of the base.

Expected value: The expected value of a random variable is the mean of its distribution.

Experimental probability: probability of an event that is found by performing the experiment multiple times.

Face value: The numerical quantity represented by the symbol for a digit.

Factor: A number, a, is said to be a factor of another number, b, if a divides b without leaving a remainder.

Fair game: A game in which each participant has the same expectation; that is, a game which does not favor any player or group of players.

Fibonacci sequence: A special sequence of numbers whose first and second terms are 1, and every successive term beginning with the third term is the sum of the previous two terms.

Figurate number: A number that can be represented by dots in some geometrical pattern.

Finite population: A well-defined set consisting of a finite number of elements, taken from a larger set. This larger set is called a population.

Five-number summary: The smallest value, the largest value, and the 3 quartile values—the first quartile, the second quartile (or median), and the third quartile—for a data set.

Fractal: A geometric figure that may result from an iterated function. Fractals typically have self-similarity, in which part of the figure is similar to larger parts of the figure. Examples include Koch's Snowflake curve and Sierpinski's triangle.

Fraction: A fraction is a number of the form a/b, where a and b are any numbers, and b $\neq$ 0.

Fractions in simplest terms: A fraction is said to be in its simplest terms if the numerator and denominator do not share a common factor.

Frequency: The number of items, or cases, falling (or expected to fall) into a category or classification.

Frequency polygon: The graph of a frequency table obtain by drawing straight lines joining successive points representing the class frequencies, plotted at the corresponding class marks. (See Frequency table)

Frequency table: A table (or other sort of arrangement) which displays the classes into which a set of data has been grouped together with the corresponding frequencies, that is the number of items falling into each class. Below is an example of a frequency table of the weights of 35 bags of beans taken from the production of a filling machine.

Weight (in pounds)	Number of Bags
12.60 - 12.79	3
12.80 - 12.99	12
13.00 - 13.19	5
13.20 - 13.39	9
13.40 - 13.59	4
13.60 - 13.79	2

Function: A correspondence between a set A (the *domain*) and a set B (the *range*) in which each element of A is paired with exactly one element of B. The table below on the left could be a function. The table on the right could not be a function because one element of the domain (1) is paired with *two* elements of the range (2 and 3).

a	b
1	2
2	5
3	2

a	b
1	2
2	5
1	3

Graph: A picture of information. In other words, a graph is a visual representation of data.

Greatest common factor: The greatest common factor of two (or more) numbers is the largest number that divides both (or all) of the numbers.

Heptagon: A polygon that has seven sides.

Hexagon: A polygon that has six sides.

Histogram: A graph of a frequency table obtained by drawing rectangles whose bases coincide with the class intervals and whose areas are proportional to the class frequencies. The sample histogram below shows the amount of money (in dollars) spent on food by a family over a 6-month period.

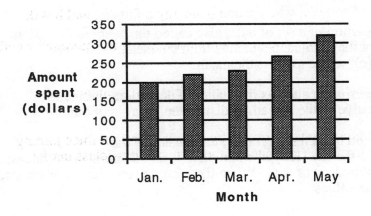

Identity: We say that a set of numbers has an identity I, under the operation *, if, for any element x in the set, we have, $I * x = x * I = x$. We call I the *-identity of the set.

Independent events: Two events A and B are independent if the occurrence of either is not affect by the occurrence or not of the other (see mutually exclusive events). If the events are not independent, they are said to be *dependent*.

Independent variable: See *dependent variable*.

Inferential statistics: Any decision, generalization, or estimate based on a sample.

Input variable: Same as *independent variable*. See *dependent variable* for a description.

Integers: The set of numbers {. . ., -3, -2, -1, 0, 1, 2, . . . }, or numbers belonging to the set.

Interquartile range: A measure of variation given by the difference between the values of the third and first quartiles of a set of data; it represents the length of the interval which contains the middle 50 per cent of the data.

Inverse: An element, say x, belonging to a set that has a *- identity, say I, is said to have a *-inverse in the set if there exists an element y in the set such that $x * y = y * x = I$.

Irrational number: A number that is not a rational number

Iterated function: A function that is "repeated" by taking the output and "feeding it back" to the function as the new input value. The first input of an iterated function is often referred to as the *seed*.

Least common multiple: The least common multiple of two (or more) numbers is the smallest number that is divisible by both (or all) of them.

Mathematical expectation: Consider the events E_1, E_2, ..., and E_k to be mutually exclusive events. Furthermore, suppose a player receives an amount of money M_1, M_2, ..., and M_k when events E_1, E_2, ..., and E_k occur respectively. If P_1, P_2, ..., P_k are the respective probabilities of these events, then the player's *mathematical expectation*–the amount of money he/she is expected to win in the long-run–is given by $E(M) = M_1P_1 + M_2P_2 + ... + M_kP_k$. In gambling game, for the game to be fair the expectation should equal the charge for playing the game.

Mean: The mean of *n* numbers is their sum divided by *n*. The mean is also know as the *arithmetic mean* or *average*.

Mean deviation: A measure of the variation of a set of data, also called the average deviation, which is given by the arithmetic mean of the absolute deviations from the mean. The mean deviation, MD, is MD= [Â |x - av(x)|]/(n), where av(x) is the mean.

Measures of variation: Statistical description such as the standard deviation, the mean deviation, or the range, which are indicative of the spread, or dispersion, of a set of data.

Median: If a list of numbers are arranged in increasing order, the median is the numerical value that marks the middle of the list. Hence, when there is an odd number of values, the median is the middle value in the ordered set of data. When there is an even number of values, the median is the mean of the two middle values.

Mode: This term is used to refer to the value which occurs with the highest frequency (most often) in a set of data. Note that a set of data can have more than one mode, or no mode at all when no two values are alike.

Multiple: A number, b, is said to be a multiple of another number, a, if a divides b without leaving a remainder.

Multiplicative: A numeration system is said to be multiplicative if each symbol in a number in that system represents a different multiple of the face value of that symbol.

Mutually exclusive events: Two events A and B are mutually exclusive if both events cannot occur at the same time.

Natural numbers: The set of counting numbers, that is, the set { 1, 2, 3, . . . }, or numbers belonging to this set.

Number: An idea that represents a numerical quantity.

Numeral: A written symbol used to represent a numerical quantity or number.

Numeration system: A system of writing numbers created to measure numerical quantities.

Octagon: A polygon that has eight sides.

Odd number: A number is said to be odd if it is not divisible by 2.

Operation: An arithmetic operation such as addition, subtraction, multiplication or division, defined on the elements of a set.

Output variable: Same as *dependent variable*.

Palindrome: A number that reads the same backward and forward.

Parallel lines: Lines in a plane that do not intersect no matter how far they are extended.

Parallelogram: A quadrilateral that has both pairs of opposite sides parallel to each other is called a parallelogram.

Pascal's Triangle: A triangular pattern of numbers, written such that the first and last term in every row is 1, and every other term in a row is the sum of the two numbers directly above it.

Pentagon: A polygon that has five sides.

Percentiles: The percentiles P_1, P_2, ..., and P_{99} are values at or below which lie, respectively, the lowest 1, 2, ..., and 99 per cent of a set of data.

Perfect number: A number is said to be perfect if the sum of all its proper factors is equal to the number.

Perimeter: The perimeter of a planar shape is the total length of its boundaries.

Permutation: Any ordered subset of a collection of n distinct objects. The number of possible permutations, each containing k objects, that can be formed from a collection of n distinct object is given by n(n-1)...(n-k+1) = (n!)/(n-k)!, and denoted $_nP_k$, P(n, k), P_k^n or $(n)_k$. For example, the number of three-digit codes that can be formed using the number 0, 1, 2, ..., 9 is (10!)/(10 - 3)! = 720.

Perpendicular lines: Lines in a plane that intersect each other at an angle of ninety degrees.

Pie graph: A graph used to represent categorical distributions, especially categorical percentage distributions. A pie graph consists of a circle subdivided into a sectors whose sizes are proportional to the quantities or percentages they represent. An example, is shown below. During Spring Break, the expenses of 3 friends went to food, drink, gas, and lodging. The pie graph shows how the money was divided among these 4 categories (in percent).

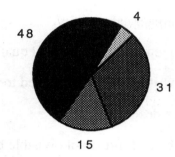

Place value: A numeration system is said to be a place value system if the value of each digit in a number in the system is determined by its position in the number. The place value of a digit is a description of its position in a given number that determines the value of the digit.

Polygon: A closed curve composed of line segments that starts and ends at the same point without crossing or retracing itself anywhere in its path is called a polygon.

Population: (See finite population, set).

Prime factorization: The decomposition of a number to express it as a product of its prime factors.

Prime number: A number that has only two factors, 1 and itself.

Probability of an event: If an event A occurs *n* times in *t* trials, the probability of event A, denoted by P(A), is

P(A) = [total occurrences of event A]/[total number of trials].

Proof: A logical, irrefutable argument to demonstrate the truth of a mathematical result.

Proportion: We say two ratios are in proportion if they represent equivalent fractions.

Pythagorean Theorem: If a right triangle has legs of lengths a and b and hypotenuse of length c, then $c^2 = a^2 + b^2$.

Quadrilateral: A polygon that has four sides is called a quadrilateral.

Quartiles: The quartiles Q_1, Q_2, and Q_3 are values at or below which lie, respectively, the lowest 25, 50, and 75 percent of a set of data.

Random event: An unbiased event.

Randomness: An indiscriminate phenomenon.

Random process: A random process, also called a stochastic process, is a process which is carried at least in part by some random mechanism.

Random sample: A sample of size n from a finite population of size N is said to be random if it is chosen so that each of the $_NC_n$ possible samples has the same probability of being selected.

Random variable: A real-valued function defined over a sample space. It is often referred to as a chance variable, a stochastic variable, or a variate. The number of tails obtained in 12 flips of a coin is an example of random variable. A capital letter, say X, is often used to denote the random variables, and a lower case letter, say x, is used to denote their values.

Range: The set of all numbers that could occur as "output values" of a function. For example, in the function

$$f(x) = \frac{1}{x-5}$$

all real numbers *except* 0 could be in the range. Note that 0 cannot be in the range because in order for the value of the function to be 0, the numerator of the fraction would have to be equal 0.

Range of data set: The range of a set of data is given by the difference between the largest value and the smallest. For instance, the range of the number 3, 1, 5, 2, and 9 is (9 -1)= 8.

Rate of change: Change in one variable, divided by the corresponding change in another variable. For example, if the temperature increases $10°$ in two hours, then the rate of change can be expressed as $5°$ per hour (i.e., $10°/2\text{hrs.} = 5°/\text{hr.}$).

Ratio: A ratio is a pair of numbers, written as a : b, with b ≠ 0.

Rational number: A rational number is a number of the form a/b, where a and b are any integers, and b ≠ 0.

Raw data: Data which has not been subjected to any sort of statistical treatment.

Ray: A ray is a collection of points all of which lie on a line, that continues indefinitely in one direction.

Rectangle: A quadrilateral whose opposite sides are of equal length and all of whose angles are ninety degrees.

Reflection: A reflection is a transformation that flips a geometrical shape over a fixed line.

Regular polygon: A polygon all of whose sides are of equal length.

Representative sample: A sample which contains the relevant characteristics of the population from which it came.

Rhombus: A quadrilateral whose opposite sides are parallel to each other, and all of whose sides are of equal length.

Right circular cone: A circular cone is the set of all points joining the circumference of a circle in a plane to a point in space, such that the line joining the point to the center of the circle is perpendicular to the plane of the circle.

Right circular cylinder: A circular cylinder is the set of all points joining the circumferences of two circles in two parallel planes such that the line joining the centers of the two circles is perpendicular to the planes of the circles.

Right rectangular prism: A solid body consisting of three pairs of congruent rectangles joined together.

Rotation: A rotation is a transformation that moves a geometrical shape around a fixed point.

Sample: The subset of a population or sample space.

Sample space: The set of points representing the possible outcomes of an experiment is called the sample space for the experiment. The sample space is often denoted by the letter S. For example, when a die is tossed the sample space is S={1, 2, 3, 4, 5, 6}.

Scatter plot: A graph used to display the relationship between two variables. The scatter plot below displays the advertising expenditures and sales volume for a company for 8 selected months (both are measured in thousands of dollars).

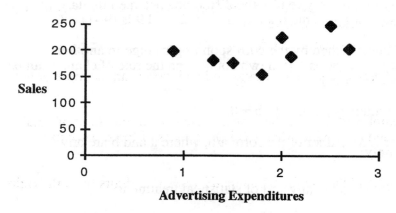

Seed: The first input value of an iterated function. For example, if we begin with 7, square it, square the new result, and so on, 7 is referred to as the seed.

Sieve of Eratosthenes: A method of finding all the prime numbers less than a given number, where numbers that are not prime are systematically crossed off a list of the natural numbers from 1 to the given number.

Similar polygons: Two polygons are said to be similar if their corresponding sides are proportional and their corresponding angles are equal.

Slope: Graphically, the "steepness" of a line. Numerically, slope is found in the same way as rate of change. It is calculated as follows:

$$slope = \frac{change\ in\ dependent\ variable}{change\ in\ independen\ t\ variable}$$

A positive slope would indicate a positive rate of change, and would appear graphically as a line slanting upward from left to right. A negative slope would indicate a negative rate of change, and would appear as a line slanting downward from left to right. A slope of zero would indicate no change in the dependent variable, and would be seen as a horizontal line.

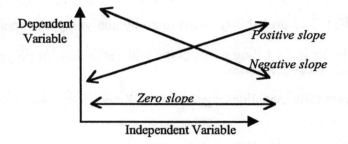

Sphere: A sphere is the set of all points in space whose distance from a fixed point also in space is constant.

Square: A quadrilateral all of whose sides are equal and all of whose angles are ninety degrees.

Standard Deviation: The standard of a sample of size n is given by the square root of the sum of the squared deviations from the mean divided by (n - 1). Some mathematicians prefer to divide by n rather than by (n-1). If a set of data has x_j elements and av(x) designates the mean of all the x_j's , for j= 1, 2, …k. then the standard deviation is given by

$$SD = Sqrt[\ (Â(\ x_j - av(x))^2)\ /\ (n\ or\ n\text{-}1)\ ],\ for\ j = 1, 2, …k.$$

Statistic: A number obtained on the basis of a sample. Standard Deviation is an example of a statistic.

Statistics: The totality of methods employed in the collection and analysis of any kind of data and, more broadly, that branch of mathematics which deals with all aspects of the science of decision making in the face of uncertainty.

Superprime: A prime number such that all the numbers obtained by deleting digits from the right of the number are still prime.

Supplementary angles: Two angles whose sum is 90 degrees are called supplementary angles.

Surface area: The surface area of a solid figure is the total area of its external surfaces.

Table: Data that have been arranged in rows and columns.

Tally chart: A chart used to record the frequency (how often) a certain piece of data occurs. Each occurrence of the piece of data is recorded by a short vertical bar. (See Frequency table). Below is an example of a tally chart.

Data	Tally	Frequency
apple	III	4
orange	III III III I	10
prune	III III II	8

Tessellation: A tessellation of the plane is the filling of the plane with repetitions of polygonal regions so that all corners meet at a vertex.

Theoretical probability: The probability determined by analyzing an experiment or situation.

Tiling: A tiling of the plane is the filling of the plane with repetitions of polygonal regions where corners do not necessarily meet at a vertex.

Translation: A transformation that slides a geometrical shape along a line segment in a given direction.

Trapezoid: A trapezoid is a quadrilateral that has one pair of opposite sides parallel to each other.

Tree diagram: A diagram in which individual paths represent all possible outcomes of an experiment.

Trial: A series of repeated experiments, such as that of tossing a die until a 5 is obtained.

Triangle: A triangle is a polygon that has three sides.

Twin primes: Two prime numbers that differ from each other by 1.

Unique representation: A numeration system is a unique representation system if each numeral refers to one and only one number.

Variable: A quality or quantity that may change or has the potential to change. For example, the amount of money in a person's savings account is variable, because it may change as a result of interest, deposits, withdrawals, and so on.

Vertical angles: Pairs of angles that are formed at the point of intersection of two intersecting lines.

Volume: The volume of a solid geometrical object is a measure of the amount of space that it encloses.

Weighted average: The average of a set of numbers obtained by multiplying each number by a weight expressing its relative importance, and then dividing the sum of these products by the sum of the weights.

Consider the set of numbers $x_1, x_2, ..., x_k$ with their respective weight $w_1, w_2, ..., w_k$. The weighted average is given by $W_a = [x_1 w_1 + x_2 w_2 ... + x_k w_k]/[w_1 + w_2 + ... + w_k]$. For example, if you work 3 hours at job A at \$18 per hour, and 5 hours at job B for \$24 per hour, then your (weighted) average earning per hour is $[(18)(3) + (5)(24)]/[8] = \$21.75$.

Whole numbers: The set of numbers {0, 1, 2, . . . }, or numbers belonging to the set.

Index